M000274763

Time:
The Ultimate Energy

Murry Hope is one of the foremost authors on esoteric wisdom, ancient magical religions and related subjects. In 1988 she established the *Institute for the Study and Development of Transpersonal Sensitivity* in America. She has published many books, run lectures and seminars, and appeared on radio and television world-wide in her capacity as an expert in this field.

By the same author
Ancient Egypt – The Sirius Connection
Atlantis – Myth or Reality?
The Book of Talimantras
The Elements of the Greek Tradition
Essential Woman: Her Mystery, Her Power
The Lion People
The Nine Lives of Tyo
Practical Celtic Magic
Practical Egyptian Magic
Practical Greek Magic
Practical Techniques of Psychic Self-Defense
The Psychology of Healing
The Psychology of Ritual
The Way of Cartouche

Time:
The Ultimate Energy

An Exploration of
the Scientific, Psychological and Metaphysical
Aspects of Time

Murry Hope

ELEMENT

Shaftesbury, Dorset • Rockport, Massachusetts

For Maureen and Gordon,
two true friends.

© Murry Hope 1991

Published in Great Britain in 1991 by
Element Books Limited
Longmead, Shaftesbury, Dorset

Published in the USA in 1991 by
Element Inc
42 Broadway, Rockport, MA 01966

All rights reserved.
No part of this book may be
reproduced or utilized in any form or by any means,
electronic or mechanical, without permission in
writing from the Publisher.

Designed by Nancy Lawrence
Cover photography: US Department of Energy/Science Photo Library
Cover design by Max Fairbrother
Typeset in 11/12 Bembo
by Footnote Graphics, Warminster, Wiltshire
Printed and bound by
Dotesios Ltd, Trowbridge, Wiltshire.

British Library Cataloguing in Publication Data

Hope, Murry
Time : the ultimate energy.
I. Title
306

ISBN 1–85230–237–2

Library of Congress Data available

Contents

Acknowledgements

My gratitude and sincere thanks to my publishers, Element Books, and Martin Jones for the use of important reference books; to Dr Charles Arthur Musès for allowing me to quote from his works; to Jed Collard, for his contribution to Chapter 2; and to theoretical physicist Peter Russell, for invaluable scientific recommendations and advice. Caduceus artwork by Martin Jones.

I am also indebted to those scientists who have made their scholarship available to general readership, without which this book, for one, could not have been written.

Foreword

The author has cut a wide swath. Here in her pages one can read of time in myth, history, and science, of time warps and slips – shades of that engrossing video drama *The Millennium*, so much better than the book on which it was based. Although the same writer did both, he had grown in perceptive stature meantime. And that, one supposes, is the best, deepest and most personal meaning of time for each of us: as the measure of our development in vision, integrity and insight. For the last is not possible without the first to begin with and the second to follow through with.

Finally, the greatest mystery of time is the ongoing significance of our own struggles, joys, sadnesses and triumphs – the ongoing destiny of ourselves as unique individuals. That that significance is not to be fractured or annulled by physical dissolution is the ultimate secret of time, one that I have addressed both scientifically and experientially.

In the following pages one is in the pronaos of time's temple and the reader is then in position to be invited to walk through the gate.

Time, since Augustine's *Confessions*, has fascinated the Western mind, and there is also a long Mahākala ('Great Time') tradition in India, intimately related to perhaps the greatest Hindu Goddess Kalī, who personifies both the destructive and the transformative power of time.

Only since the advent of quantum physics and the related concepts of antitime and resonance, in cybernetic theory and higher mathematics, are we on the brink of a new and revolutionary approach to time waves as the ultimate energy source. I have termed this new approach Chronotopology.

Since I have published on these subjects in scientific books and journals, I am happy to endorse this investigative work on time as a real stimulant and help to the lay public interested in approaching some of these matters in more popular fashion.

Dr C. Musès
Director Mathematics and Morphology Research Centre

Introduction

Time is something we all take for granted without necessarily analysing exactly what it is. We know that as time passes we grow older; our bodies undergo many changes, while our attitudes to life and our mental outlook are definitely coloured by what has taken place during the passage of time. The subject of time has fascinated the enquiring mind since the dawn of civilization as we know it, and, as I hope to show, prior to the times of recorded history. We hear or read references to 'corridors of time', 'arrows of time', and so forth. Are these simply figures of speech, or do they contain a more profound meaning which relates to the deeper aspects of both human psychology and the life cycles of all living creatures?

The rapidly expanding fields of quantum, particle and astro-physics are slowly opening up a new understanding of the nature and function of time, both in relation to the physical universe and those more subtle dimensions of which scientists are starting to catch the occasional fleeting glimpse. But is our use of particle accelerators in nuclear research, and similar technological gadgetry, actually limiting our ability to understand the broader significance of time? The creation most suited to probing time's subtle secrets is the human mind, which could, were its cranial computer to be suitably programmed, produce more astounding revelations.

The planet upon which we live and the myriad life forms it sustains, in keeping with everything else in the universe, are subject to that cosmic law which designates the continuing cycle of change. Some may view this in terms of pendulum-like swings between chaos and order, others classify it as evolution, while ancient civilizations accorded it a feminine identity – a goddess of destruction and regeneration, whose name varied with each archaic pantheon. But if we ask ourselves, what is the prime force

1

behind these ever-continuing cycles, leaving aside the physical phenomena that are the tools of its enactment and the personalized forces of retribution to which religion accredits it, the answer must surely be *time*. We are told that time heals all; that time decides the outcome of our actions, hopes and wishes, and that time is the inevitable reaper from the swing of whose scythe nothing or no one is exempted. Time can change our outlook, our opinions, our beliefs and if, like the proverbial reed, we do not bend with the winds of time we suffer the consequences. In fact, time would appear to manipulate us both psychologically and physically.

At this point in the evolutionary history of our planet our concept of the nature of time has mostly been dictated by the subjective experiences of our life cycles. We tend to view time in linear terms, as applicable to our own planet and solar system, and the birth of the physical universe. In relation to our everyday lives this cycle manifests in birth, growth, maturity, ageing, and eventually death. It is absolute and irrevocable, and it is something over which at present we have no control. In the ensuing pages, however, I propose to show that time is actually multiaspected, although most of its manifestations could be seen to slot into two broad categories. There is the linear time we see on our clocks, which is decided by the movement of our planet, both on its own axis and in relation to its mother-sun, and which appears to operate predictably and in a predetermined way; this I call *Inner Time*. The non-linear time that exists beyond the confines of our own little corner of the universe I refer to as *Outer Time*. Inner Time will obviously manifest according to the physical conditions dictated by the movement of bodies within any given cosmic vicinity, in the Earth's case its movement in relation to the sun. Outer Time, on the other hand, not being subject to physical conditions as such, also embraces timelessness, and those subtle dimensions that are not concerned with the worlds of matter, about which our knowledge is purely speculative and therefore more metaphysical than physical.

Few people have, to date, been 'programmed' to understand and appreciate Outer Time, although scientists can offer some very impressive-looking equations for its existence which I have heard described as being 'more esoteric than a guru'! However, who or whatever originally designed our brains must have been fully cognizant with the nature of Outer Time, and the forthcoming quantum leaps that would eventually effect the mental and physical activation required to accommodate a full and comprehensive understanding of it.

It is my own belief that different areas of the brain probably become activated during what are referred to as 'evolutionary quantum leaps' (see p. 43), and that one such area, which has yet to be defined, holds the key to the comprehension of Outer Time. Once the time-code has been cracked, vast energy fields, the nature and breadth of which we may not even have dreamed of, will be available for our use and we can only guess at which direction our handling of these powers may take once we have familiarized ourselves with their existence and obvious usefulness. But, of course, having conquered 'the enemy' and finally freed ourselves from the chains of Inner Time that have constituted our bondage during the particular evolutionary cycle through which we have been passing, we will, we hope, be wiser, more sensitive, and more spiritually mature.

As a metaphysician, one of my tasks is to effect a correlation between the various philosophic, scientific, and mystical systems and schools of thought that might possibly help to open the way to a more holistic view of our subject matter. So, while I shall obviously be referring to the knowledge and theories currently favoured by the scientific establishment, I also aim to give space to some of the less orthodox hypotheses on time and the universe that have not originated from the minds of the giants of cosmology and physics. History has, after all, tended to confirm that major discoveries are not exclusive to the erudite, or those who, by qualification, are at the pinnacle of their respective professions. Besides, truth is not the prerequisite of any one creed, philosophy or science, and sometimes the outside observer is able to get a better view of the whole picture than the specialist who is busy scrutinizing the individual brush-strokes.

If you are curious about your own future and the future of your planet, and how you yourselves, your children and grandchildren are going to cope with the forthcoming evolutionary quantum jump that will catapult us all into an entirely new time-cycle, then read on. Frightening it might appear at first glance, but if you can enter it in the spirit of adventure, it could prove to be the most stimulating and exciting experience you are ever likely to undergo in the bosom of Gaia.

Part 1

Facts and Theories

1
What is Time

What's past, and what's to come is strew'd with husks
And formless ruins of oblivion.
The end crowns all,
And that old common arbitrator, Time,
Will one day end it.

SHAKESPEARE (Troilus and Cressida)

Time is something that many of us have tended to take for granted. It simply *is*, and we cannot conceive of an existence outside the ordered state of our cosy little, time-regulated world. Any mention of Outer Time is treated purely as a science-fiction spin-off that is not to be taken seriously, while on those occasions when science does offer tangible proof, fear rears its ugly head. Although for centuries the majority of people have accepted without question time as it manifests on this planet, viewing it either as the handiwork of some favoured divinity or a law of nature, there have always been the few – philosophers, scientists, metaphysicians, and the curious – who have probed beyond Inner Time for the answers to the many riddles proposed by the veiled aspects of the cosmos. However, before we embark on our journey into the highways and byways of Outer Time, a comprehensive analysis of Inner Time will not go amiss, as it may help many of us to understand those physical laws that we accept so easily simply because we are more familiar with their manifestations.

Paradigms

Our measurement of time was for many years determined by the period of rotation of the Earth relative to the astronomical bodies. For example, we have *solar time* which is measured by successive intervals between transits of the sun across the meridian, and is shown on a sundial; *mean solar time*, which averages out this interval over the course of one year and is employed in day-to-day work. The solar day begins at midnight. The *mean sun* is a point that moves uniformly around the celestial equator in the same total time as the real sun takes round the ecliptic. The difference between apparent and mean solar time, up to sixteen minutes, is known as the *equation of time*. Then there is *sidereal time*, which is measured by successive transits of the first point of Aries d across the meridian, and is indicated by the position of astronomical bodies relative to the horizon; *mean sidereal time* averages out this interval over the course of one year and is employed by astronomers. Following on from this, we have the *solar year*, (or *tropical year*), the *solar month* and the *solar day*; the *sidereal year*, the *sidereal month* and the *sidereal day*, and finally the *calendar year* (or *civil year*) which is adjusted so that its length is that of the average solar year.[1] Recently, however, atomic clocks have provided us with far more precise measurements of Inner Time.

The aforegoing shows us the basis of the time we accept as a natural, everyday occurence. In simple language, it is 9.00 a.m. or 5.30 p.m. for us because of the position of the moving orb upon which we live in relation to other obvious points of reference in the universe at any given moment. Since this apparently well-regulated form of time has prevailed for so many thousands of years, we have come to accept its rigidity as a secure factor to which life upon this planet entitles us. Centuries of observation have decreed that we acknowledge the sequence of events that take place in our lives as having some semblance of order. We look back and note how things have changed and how, in fact, we ourselves have emerged from that corridor of time that has constituted our life to date, becoming the people we are at present. Likewise, we may observe that old Father Time has also exerted a profound effect upon the world in which we live, leaving his very distinctive footprints across the pages of our past history. This naturally gives rise to the logical conclusion that time is linear. Like a river it flows, and we are swept along with the many broken branches, silt, waste products, and other flotsam that it carries down to the mighty sea of the future. Such is our subjective view of time, which can be seen as confirmed in the scientific premise that the universe as a whole is engaged in *unidirectional change*, sometimes referred to symbolically as an 'arrow of time' that points from the past to the future.

Arrows of Time

The phrase 'arrow of time' was coined in 1927 by the British astronomer Sir Arthur Eddington, an astrophysicist and expert on general relativity, who popularized and helped prove Einstein's Theory of Relativity. It encapsulates the idea that time, like an arrow from a bow, moves irreversibly forward. But pure observation is insufficient proof to scientists that this is necessarily so, since the great laws of physics, Einstein's Theory of Relativity, for example, and the atom-smashing quantum mechanics of Heisenberg and Schrödinger, have no arrow of time in the essentially forward direction as subjective experience might suggest, and would work just as well if time moved backwards. Since Eddington's time, the term 'arrow', or 'arrows' of time has appeared regularly in scientific parlance, and as a title for books and programmes in the popular media.

Newton's Theory

Over the years science has presented us with some rather contradictory paradigms. For example, in his monumental work *Principia Mathematica*, published in 1687, the British physicist Sir Isaac Newton (1642–1727) introduced, in the form of precise mathematical equations, his three famous laws that govern the motion of material bodies (see Glossary, Newton's Laws of Motion). If these laws are as absolute and fixed as some scientists have been inclined to believe, the inference would be that all events within the universe are either fixed or prefixed. The implications of Newton's 'clockwork universe' were quickly realized by the nineteenth-century French physicist the Marquis Pierre de Laplace, who commented:

> Consider an intelligence which, at any instant, could have a knowledge of all forces controlling nature together with the momentary conditions of all the entities of which nature consists. If this intelligence were powerful enough to submit all this data to analysis it would be able to embrace in a single formula the movements of the largest bodies in the universe and those of the lightest atoms; for it nothing would be uncertain; the future and the past would be equally present to its eyes. [2]

The conclusion to be drawn from Laplace's statement would be that everything that has ever happened in the whole universe, at all levels, everything that is happening now, and everything that will occur in the future has been predetermined from the first instant of time. So, although we may view the years ahead with a degree of uncertainty, since future events are already fixed any efforts to change them would constitute a waste of time. The alternative interpretation, often proffered by metaphysicians, counters with the suggestion that since everything is laid down in the blueprint, our decisions and the results of our actions are already known and thus contribute an essential ingredient to the overall plan.

This 'determinism' of Newtonian mechanics has found so much favour with scientists over the years that it still forms the basis of scientific testing according to the laws of theoretical physics. In other words, since physical realities are seen to be mirrored in mathematical equations, the theoretical physicist is able to gain a reasonably accurate idea of conditions in outer space, for example, simply by effecting the correct calculations. Such computations have, in fact, proved the cornerstone of our space explorations to date, the degree of accuracy being calculated to a fraction of a second.

For many years, the Newtonian concept of absolute time became so ingrained in our lives that the initial introduction of daylight saving time in 1916 resulted in an outcry that mankind was interfering with 'God's time', which was believed by many to be unequivocal and sacrosanct. Since Newton's day, however, the old Newtonian concepts have undergone considerable amplification and modification. Major strides in scientific research and subsequent discoveries have resulted in fundamental material entities no longer being considered as particles, recent ideas favouring the concept of energy *fields* in which particles are the disturbing factors. In spite of this, the Newtonian paradigm still stands firm for many, the activity of 'fields' being viewed as conforming to its rules. At the same time our ever-expanding fount of knowledge of space, time and matter, which has resulted from the escalating quantum and relativity revolutions, has also accommodated the Newtonian doctrine of determinism.

However, since Newtonian Time is concerned with the laws of motion, which are seen as being reversible in that they do not distinguish between 'forwards' and 'backwards' – time's arrow can point in either direction – and therein lies the paradox. Working on this assumption, we should be able to restore a fallen wall or regain our youth simply by winding time backwards in the same way that a roll of film can be reversed. To the rationally minded, of course, this is nothing short of ridiculous and merits immediate dismissal, although some may keep an open mind regarding its theoretical value. One logical example offered by physicist Dr John Gribbin, is that of a tennis player standing still and bouncing a tennis ball on the ground repeatedly with his racket. Were this activity to be filmed and played backwards the viewers would see nothing odd about it because the act of bouncing the ball is reversible, or 'time symmetric'. But were that same person to be filmed lighting a bonfire, and the film reversed, it would be obvious to all viewers that something was wrong. This is because the bonfire-making process is 'irreversible' – it exhibits an asymmetry in time.

So, we may ask, why the difference? It is, we are told, simply a question of time. The tennis player will eventually die of old age long before the tennis ball wears out, although, taking into account the number of new balls used at any major tennis tournament one might see fit to question this. However, I think we get the point Dr Gribbin is trying to make. Even the example of our planets orbiting round the sun is not really reversible; changes in their orbits could be effected by external courses; the rotation of the Earth might vary, or the moon move further away from its parent planet. All of these effects could, however, be detected by a physicist using equipment that was sufficiently sensitive to this type of phenomenon and in so doing deduce the existence of the arrow of time moving in one direction only. The conundrums commence, of course, when we come to the world of minute particles, wherein time appears to be reversed and the arrow of time points in a very different direction. Explaining these subtle differences in time direction calls for some highly complex equations, backed by more examples than space permits in this book. The technically-minded enquirer is referred to the bibliography for the relevant works of the scientists concerned. Bearing this question of symmetry in mind, however, one cannot help wondering whether the fact that a past event is 'time symmetric' or reversible, makes it easier for sensitive, psychic, or mediumistic people to tune into and interpret, whereas an asymmetrical or irreversible occurence might defeat them, as the tendency would be to apply a natural monitoring logic which could result in a subconscious, if not an actual conscious rejection of the viewing. There are some well-documented examples of this which have been duly noted by parapsychologists working in the fields of research.

Entropy

Professor Paul Davies sees the answer to those multidirectional

arrows of time as residing in the Second Law of Thermodynamics.
He tells us:

> When we put ice in warm water, the water melts the ice, because heat
> flows from the warm liquid into the cold ice. The reverse process,
> where the heat flows out of the ice making the water even warmer, is
> never observed. These ideas were made precise by defining a quantity
> called *entropy*, which can be thought of, very roughly, as a measure of
> the potency of heat energy.'[3]

Thermodynamics, the study of the interrelationship between heat
and other forms of energy, is only concerned with changes of
energy and not with the mechanisms by which that change is
effected, and is based on three fundamental 'laws'. This 'second
law' to which Davies refers, involves what is known as *entropy*
which comes from the Greek *en* (in) and *trope* (turning). In simple
language entropy could be described as a transition from order to
disorder, or dissolution following organization, but for the benefit
of the more technically-minded reader, a full scientific definition is
given in the Glossary.

Entropy alone among the laws of physics includes the directional
arrow of time. I have introduced the entropy principle at this early
stage because, aside from its more obvious functions, it also
appears to have 'octaves' which resonate at psychological and
metaphysical levels, especially as related to time within the more
subtle frequencies. But more of that later.

Chaos

The next player to enter the space-time arena is Chaos Science,
viewed by many physicists as a major revolution which de-
molishes the tenets of Newtonian physics and, as one scientist has
put it: 'Relativity eliminated the Newtonian illusion of absolute
space and time; quantum theory eliminated the Newtonian dream
of a controllable measurement process; and chaos eliminates the
Laplacian fantasy of deterministic predictability.'[4]

Writing on the subject of Chaos Science James Gleick tells
us:

> *Where chaos begins*, classical science stops. For as long as the world has
> had physicists inquiring into the laws of nature, it has suffered a
> special ignorance about disorder in the atmosphere, in the turbulent
> sea, in the fluctuations of wildlife populations, in the oscillations of the
> heart and brain. The irregular side of nature, the discontinuous and

erratic side – these have been puzzles to science, or worse, monstrosities.[5]

Our cosy little, time-regulated world suddenly begins to take on a new aspect. Are we, in fact, being psychologically prepared for the next manifestation of the 'chaos principle'? In the ensuing chapters I hope to show the reality of chaos, and how what we view as vast areas of time are, in fact, less than the blink of a cosmic eyelid. All creation oscillates between order and chaos. We have, perhaps, been fortunate in that for the last few centuries our planet has been experiencing a period of orderliness as far as the time factor is concerned. But those Greek sages who maintained that the Earth shifted on its axis every 10,000 years, or there-abouts, must have been familiar with the chaos–order conflict that governs all levels of existence from base matter to those invisible wavebands that are, for the present anyway, perceptible only to those intelligences receptive to the higher frequencies of conciousness. I hesitate to add the word 'human' here, as it is my fervent belief that many of the life forms with which we share this planet, and Gaia herself for that matter, are capable of a more profound understanding of the transcendental frequencies than we might have hitherto imagined.

In their book *The Arrow of Time*, *Daily Telegraph* science editor Dr Roger Highfield, and his co-author Dr Peter Coveney, a lecturer in Physical Chemistry at the University of Wales, comment on the unpredictability indicated by chaos, which they see as providing the justification for the 'arrow of time' as a unifying factor. They are of the opinion that many of the laws that scientists have held dear have been proven to be selective rather than universal, which indicates that a new understanding is called for in which, perhaps, time forms a central thread. In an interview with Eric Bailey, in The *Daily Telegraph: Weekend* (11 August 1990), Coveney states: 'Far from being on the verge of a complete understanding of nature, we may be on the threshold of a radically new framework in which time occupies a central rather than a marginal role.' The suggestion is that aesthetics and spirituality may need to be combined with traditional scientific thought in order to achieve answers. Coveney tells us that in Newton's universe, God would simply have had to light a blue touch paper and retire, whereas these new scientific ideas emphasize creativity, innovation and free will. Logic, as such, has therefore reached its limits, and we will need more than left-brain reasoning to understand the subtle and powerful world of time.

Relativity

There was a young lady named Bright,
Whose speed was much faster than light,
She set out one day,
In a relative way,
To return on the previous night!

This amusing little limerick has doubtless evoked a laugh from scientist and layman alike, but to many the reality of the existence of a different time from what they are used to, and can mentally compute, is anything but reassuring. However, since time in all its apparent complexities is subject to certain natural laws that we are slowly beginning to understand, it should be divested of its mystique and a practical appraisal made of its potential as a potent force in our planet's future.

Relativity, a theory of relative motion, space and time was the brainchild of Albert Einstein, the German-born mathematician-physicist who, at the age of twenty-six, demolished the 300-year-old idea of absolute time, overturning the entire foundations of classical Newtonian physics and replacing them with a revolutionary assessment of a new reality in which time and space took on a new meaning. Einstein's theory appeared in two parts, the first of which was published in 1905, and is now known as the Special Theory of Relativity, while the second instalment, published in 1915, is known as the General Theory of Relativity. Special Relativity developed from two principles: first, that the laws of natural phenomena are the same for all observers; and second, that the velocity of light is constant for all observers regardless of their own velocity. From these two basic principles Einstein deduced that mass and energy are interchangeable, and are related by the well-known formula $E = mc^2$. ('E' is energy, 'm' is mass, and 'c', is the speed of light.) The formula shows that a small mass can be converted into a huge amount of energy, hence the saying 'all matter is frozen energy'. This idea led to, among other things, the invention of nuclear weapons and the development of thermonuclear power, while also explaining those processes of nuclear fusion that take place on the sun and are responsible for its heat and light. One consequence of Special Relativity, which specifically affects the concept of simultaneity, is *time dilation*. According to this phenomenon, if two observers are moving at constant velocity relative to each other, it will appear to each that the other's clocks have slowed down.

In the General Relativity theory, Einstein showed that the

presence of massive bodies in space – or more specifically the presence of their gravitational fields – distorts space itself, so that the shortest distance between two points becomes a curve rather than a straight line. Light also is bent by the gravitational field of a massive body. Recent discoveries in astrophysics and nuclear physics, as well as knowledge gained from space exploration, have tended to vouch for the validity of Einstein's work.

Einstein's theory proposes that all motion is relative and that absolute rest is meaningless; or to put it simply, rest and motion do not exist by themselves, they depend on comparing one object with another. This whole proposition is particularly relevant to any study of time as it takes into consideration the curvature of space-time, time dilation and other phenomena associated with both Inner and Outer Time, such as the possible juncture at which one becomes the other. Also, and this is important to my own premise, the third factor involved in the process by which mass is converted to energy – even if it be only a fleeting second or so – is *Time*!

All Einstein's equations are said to possess in broad terms the same deterministic structure and time-reversible features as Newton's mechanics. There is, for example, no distinction between forward moving time and time running backwards. It is this premise that makes time travel feasible and why, according to Highfield and Coveney, an *ad hoc* assertion needs to be introduced to ban it on the grounds that it could undermine all those notions of cause and effect associated with the 'arrow of time' theory. I am at a loss to understand why this should be necessary unless, of course, our learned friends are endeavouring to bring the chaotic and liberated world of quantum theory into line with the limited dimensions of earthly logic. Anomalies in these and other frequencies associated with the backward/forward motions of time there certainly are, and what we are dealing with here probably equates with the old metaphysical belief that the waveband of each frequency has its own laws, which do not necessarily apply to the worlds of its neighbours. However, we shall be examining some of those paradoxes that appear to clash with time's forward moving arrow, and overstep the boundaries of logic, in Chapter 3.

A Grand Unified Theory?

In recent years several attempts have been made to formulate a Grand Unified Theory (GUT) which unites the properties of gravitational, electromagnetic, and nuclear fields so that a single set of equations could be used to predict all their characteristics, but so far nothing concrete has been achieved in this direction. Commenting on this fact, Professor Stephen Hawking asks us whether there can really be such a unified theory, or are we perhaps just chasing a mirage? He indicates there seem to be three possibilities:

1. There really is a complete unified theory, which we will someday discover if we are smart enough.
2. There is no ultimate theory of the universe, just an infinite sequence of theories that describe the universe more and more accurately.
3. There is no theory of the universe; events cannot be predicted beyond a certain extent but occur in a random and arbitrary manner.[6]

Hawking views the possible limitations in terms of Heisenberg's Uncertainty Principle of quantum mechanics, and the fact that we could not solve equations of the theory exactly 'except in very simple situations'.

It seems logical to me that there must be some universal point in time and space where all energy fields unite, that could be expressed via the main fundamental concepts of twentieth-century physics, quantum theory and relativity. But since it is highly likely that there are other potential sources of energy that have yet to be discovered (or rediscovered?) and utilized, no doubt a fair piece of the jigsaw is still missing. In their book *From Quarks to the Cosmos* Dr Leon M. Lederman, who shared the 1988 Nobel prize in physics for the discovery of the muon neutrino, and Dr David N. Schramm, would appear to be thinking along similar lines with their TOE – 'theory of everything' – although they admit that enormous energies will be required to unify the 'four forces of nature' (see illustration).[7]

Heisenberg's Uncertainty Principle

This is also called the Principle of Indeterminism, and reflects the inability to predict the future based on the past or present. First proposed by Werner Heisenberg (1901–76) around 1926 or 1927, it has become the cornerstone of quantum physics and provides an understanding of why the world is made up of events that cannot be related entirely to the laws of cause and effect. In quantum terms, it claims that one can never be exactly sure of both the position and velocity of a particle, since it is impossible to obtain

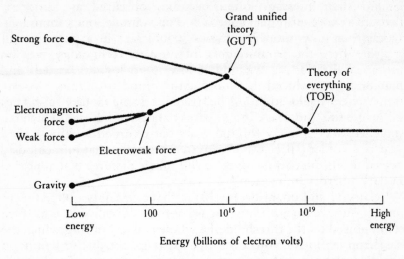

Energy (billions of electron volts)

Enormous energies are required to unify the four forces of nature. It is thought the four forces were once unified at the higher energies characteristic of the universe soon after the Big Bang, and indeed a theory that unifies the weak force and the electromagnetic force has already been verified for energies of a few hundred GeV.

an accurate assessment of both, which evoked from British physicist Sir Arthur Eddington the amusing comment: 'Something unknown is doing we don't know what!' This principle, however, is by no means limited to the world of matter; it has also been observed to work equally via the human psychology, through which it manifests as doubts and insecurities.

Extending this principle into the metaphysical world, I would add: how much of the universe we are able to discover at any one time will depend on the evolutionary stage through which the planet (Gaia, in our case) is passing, and the effect that particular phase is likely to have upon the thinking patterns of the dominant species to which that planet has given life.

Of course, I am not a physicist, but as a metaphysician I view all scientific theories, discoveries and equations in terms of principles which can be visualized and categorized with the right-brain hemisphere and logically translated into terms of reference easily recognizable to the layman by the left brain. Sages, philosophers and other wise people have indulged in this practice over many centuries, often employing parable, myth or fairy-tale to convey more complex hypotheses and their relative equations. The only fault in this procedure lies in the fact that the real significance behind their message often becomes obscured as 'progress' favours a more empirical approach. For example, one cannot help wondering how modern physics would fare in a post-axis tilt world where the ironmongery of modern technology was no more, civilization as we now know it no longer existed, and mankind was reduced to a more natural mode of living. Generations hence would doubtless be treated to some fantasy sci-fi tales of 'magic fire' (nuclear energy), trips to fairyland during which the travellers stayed away for 100 years but returned looking only a year or so older (space travel), mysterious boxes that miraculously heated food (microwave ovens), and magic pictures that appeared in dark mirrors (television)!

Relativity and quantum mechanics have certainly obliged us to review our previous commonsense notions of reality. It is as if we stand poised on the threshold of a whole new era during which the basic conventions of our everyday existence are due to be turned upside down, or replaced with a dramatically new order that will require considerable mental adjustment or, as I prefer to say, a radical reprogramming of that marvellous computer – the human brain – in which an entirely new series of hitherto unused circuits are brought into play. We will be obliged to adjust ourselves to the fact that there is no absolute sequence of moments and no objective way of ordering events in time. According to some interpretations of general relativity, time may be circular or even spiral, so that journeys into the past and future are theoretically possible. With the esoteric microworld of elementary particles continually shattering the foundations of scientific knowledge, any previous notions we might have harboured as to the temporal ordering of time become less tenable. Time, in fact, is assuming increasingly an enigmatic role in both our present and future, and sooner or later we will be obliged to accept for a fact that all time is really one. Everything exists in the Eternal Now, and it will be at that point of understanding that physics will meet metaphysics; past, present and future will be seen in a singular context, and the real value of *time as an energy itself* will be finally acknowledged.

The concept of relativity as related to either space travel, or Outer Time, has given rise to numerous examples as to how this might work on a practical basis. One such scenario was set by Dr J. M. Stuart of the Department of Applied Mathematics and Theoretical Physics at the University of Cambridge. On the 19 April 1978, under the *nom de plume* of Athene Williams, which belonged to a particular column I wrote at the time, I was privileged to be included in a broadcast on Radio 4 with Dr Stuart and fellow scientist Dr Lyall Watson.

Commencing with the comment that what he was about to say might make the adventures of television's famous Time Lord, Dr Who, appear rather simple, Dr Stuart asked his listeners to imagine a father and son, both of whom were astronauts, who proceed to investigate a very dense world somewhere in space which has a very strong gravitational field. The father decides that he will not descend to the surface of the planet but stay in the orbiting spacecraft well away from its strong gravitational field, while his son goes below in his mini-craft to effect his investigations. After staying for two weeks the son returns to the mother ship, but because the planet that he has been visiting has a far stronger gravitational field than the parent ship, his physical processes will have been speeded up so that he has aged much more quickly than his father. The son believes he has been away for a fortnight, but the father sees his son's absence as having been considerably longer. Since the son will have aged at a greater rate than the father, they could both be faced with the ludicrous situation that upon his return the son actually finds himself older than his parent!

Stuart apparently based his hypothesis on a classic experiment that dated from the 1960s when a very accurate atomic clock was placed at the top and another at the bottom of a tower at Harvard University, and it was observed that the clock at the top went a fraction more slowly than the one at the bottom. Transfer this concept to outer space and Dr Stuart's theory enters the realms of possibility. The kind of space travel envisioned by many scientists would involve craft travelling at or beyond the speed of light, approximately 186,000 miles (300,000 kilometres) per second in a vacuum, believed to be the ultimate speed limit in the universe, and popularly referred to as photon power. The light spectrum extends from radio waves of very low frequency to gamma rays from radioactive substances, of very high frequency and dangerous to living things. Within its narrow part of the spectrum, light varies in colour depending on the frequency or length of its waves, from comparatively low frequency red through orange, yellow, green, and blue, to high frequency violet. One cannot help wondering what colour or colours would confront the vision of those astronauts travelling on photon power?

The Quantum Theory

This theory concerns the behaviour of physical systems based on the idea that they can only possess certain properties, such as energy and angular momentum, in discrete amounts (quanta), 'discrete' in this context meaning separate or distinct, or consisting of separate or distinct parts. In physics, the term 'quantum' refers to the smallest quantity of some physical property that a system can possess according to the quantum theory. Quantum mechanics is the branch of science based on the quantum theory: it is used for interpreting the behaviour of elementary particles and atoms which do not obey Newtonian mechanics.

So why are the quantum worlds so important to the study and understanding of time? Quantum systems conquer space and time because particles interact over distances without any discernible link – an action known to physicists as 'non-locality'. Quantum waves of matter also contain an infinite number of possibilities, referred to as the 'Uncertainty Principle', (see p. 16) until they eventually form into conglomerates of particles. But the most interesting aspect is that particles of matter the size of atoms and smaller appear to operate according to a different set of rules to the rest of nature. These rules, which were first presented in modern form by Erwin Shrödinger and Werner Heisenberg in the 1920s, are known collectively as 'quantum mechanics'.

In quantum mechanics, each particle has ascribed to it a 'wave' that can be described by a wave equation, in much the same way as any other wave. This is known as the Shrödinger equation for the particle. In classical (large-scale) situations it is easy to appreciate the value and meaning of wave equations; for example, water waves travelling across a pond have both an amplitude (height) and a phase. Solutions to the Shrödinger equations are different, however. Although they are still referred to in terms of amplitudes, lengths and phases, the proper square of the amplitude of the wave becomes the probability of the particle being somewhere or taking part in some quantum mechanical process.

In the same way that microscopic particles, such as electrons, can act as waves, so also can light (which would normally be considered as wave-like) exhibit what is known as 'corpuscular properties' under appropriate conditions. These quantum corpuscles of light are known as photons and, in fact, all electromagnetic radiation at any frequency can be thought of as consisting of discrete photons. (See also p. 19 and p. 42–3).

Following the Second World War, the American physicist, Dr Richard Feynman, introduced his concept of quantum electrodynamics, which was set up to describe the interaction of light with microscopically electrically charged particles such as

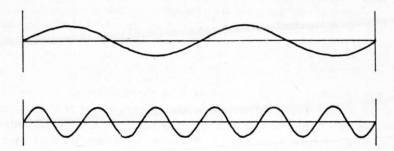

electrons. Feynman's quantum electrodynamics, based on the earlier work of Schrödinger and Heisenberg, consists of wave particles of charged matter interacting with wave particles of light. These ideas appeared bizarre when they were first introduced in the 1920s and even today it can be truthfully stated that no one really understands how quantum mechanics works, but it does.

However, not all scientists share the same view regarding microscopic reversibility and irreversibility, notably Ilya Prigogine, who attacked the problem of reconciling the two. Prigogine was born in Moscow in 1917, but has been associated with the Free University of Brussels since 1947, and more recently with the University of Texas (Austin). He received the Nobel prize for Chemistry in 1977 for his work in non-equilibrium thermodynamics, although his ideas have been slow in filtering into the textbooks. Dr John Gribbin, writing in the *Guardian* (5 February, 1988) in an article dealing with the arrow of time, entitled 'Mainspring of the Universe', leaned on the Prigogine theory to explain why we cannot, after all, put the clock back:

> There are two key features of quantum physics that are relevant to the thermodynamics of the Universe.
>
> First, the equations of quantum physics, like those of classical physics, are time-symmetric. That seems to leave us with the same conflict between the reversibility of Newtonian mechanics and the ageing of the real world. But the second feature of the new physics gets us off that hook.
>
> Werner Heisenberg discovered that the equations do not allow us to make a precise measurement of both the position and the momentum of a particle at the same time. We cannot know, as a matter of principle, exactly where a particle is *and* where it is going. We can

determine either property on its own as accurately as we like, but the
more precisely we measure position the less information we have
about momentum and vice versa . . .

   No matter how long we sit and watch a lukewarm cup of coffee, it
will never spontaneously give birth to an ice cube and heat up; no
matter how long we sit by a box of gas, it will never all congregate in
one half of the box, so that we can trap it in a state of lower entropy.
The arrow of time is an absolute feature of the Universe.

Hawking refers to there being at least three different arrows of
time: 1. The thermodynamic arrow of time – the direction of
time in which disorder or entropy increases;   2. The psychological arrow of time – this is the direction in which we feel time
passes; and   3. The cosmological arrow of time – the direction of
time in which the universe is expanding rather than contracting.[8]
But more concerning number 3 in the next chapter.

   Recent discoveries in quantum mechanics have opened the door
to a whole new world of minute particles, some of which are
observed to occupy no space at all. But as Heisenberg so wisely
observed, 'the senses are not an adequate guide to the way the
world works – in such matters language is useless.' The television
programme 'QED', of 14 February 1990, dealt specifically with
particle physics as related to time. High-speed particle acceleration, it is believed, may well provide some of the answers to the
question of what happens to a particle when it exceeds a certain
speed. Some theories favour the idea that there could be a point at
which time actually reverses. Various aspects of time were discussed, including the fact that the faster one goes the slower time
passes, time travel via high speed neutron rotating stars, and a host
of other titillating morsels for the space-time conscious viewer to
think about.

   Today we may view such phenomena with a degree of incredulity,
but since history has tended to support the idea that the science
fiction of one era becomes the science fact of the next, no doubt
future generations will accept such things as the manipulation of
time in much the same way that we have adjusted to videos and
microchips. Perhaps Einstein had the right idea when he said: 'The
most incomprehensible thing about the Universe is that it is
comprehensible.' Obviously, we still have a lot to learn about its
basic structure and rules which, when analysed, will no doubt turn
out to be quite straightforward.

   An examination of current theories and beliefs of the more
orthodox schools of science has been essential to this book before
moving into more speculative fields of enquiry, as it provides a

backcloth against which the later premises can be weighed and assessed. No doubt, many of the theories currently favoured by the scientific establishment will change as we progress through time, for not all of those qualified in their disciplines see time in the same frame as Newton or Einstein. Anthropologist/zoologist Dr Lyall Watson, who because of his fearless thinking and metaphysical leanings is fast becoming a legend in his own time, conceives of time as existing in stationary bands through which we pass. His brilliant Shattered Hologram theory (see Chapter 8) encompasses both the premises and theories of orthodox science and those of metaphysics. It is my own belief that any genuine scientific fact should reverberate at or resonate with other, more subtle, aspects of life, such as psychology and those physically imperceptible wavebands that are at present only identifiable by the mind via the right hemisphere of the brain.

In her book *The Quantum Self*, Oxford physicist Danah Zohar has enlarged upon this concept, suggesting that consciousness is a quantum-physical system, keeping every living thing in intimate and constant interaction with others, with nature, with history and with God; but more of this also in Chapter 8. Writing in *The Nature of Things*, Lyall Watson extends this concept even further, embracing the ancient belief in animism. Recent developments on the Earth's surface, which have in many cases been precipitated by mankind, have tended to confirm both these premises. Professor Sir James Lovell's Gaia Hypothesis adds the final touch to the reality of the intricately woven web of *all* life, of which we, as *Homo sapiens*, are but one small part.

Endnotes

1. *A Dictionary of Physics*, pp. 383–4.
2. Paul Davies, *The Cosmic Blueprint*, p. 10.
3. *Ibid.* p. 15.
4. J. Gleick, *Chaos*, p. 6.
5. *Ibid.* p .3.
6. S. W. Hawking, *A Brief History of Time* pp. 165–6.
7. L. M. Lederman and D. N. Schramm, *From Quarks to the Cosmos*, p. 160.
8. S. W. Hawking, *A Brief History of Time*, p. 145.

2
Time and the Universe

The ultimate significance of time is its transience – this has been called 'absolute becoming'.
G. J. WHITROW

When we look into a blue or cloud-patched sky, or a starry night firmament, we may perceive a tiny portion of what is referred to as the universe. But how can we be sure that what we see is *the only* universe and, assuming, as many scientists and metaphysicians do, that there may well be *other* universes, why is our particular view limited to just the one? The metaphysician would naturally counter with the reply: 'Easy, you see what you see because you resonate at the same frequency as that particular universe. Now were you to exist at another frequency, you would probably find this universe totally imperceptible.' But what has science to say about all this? Are there, for example, more subtle universes, the presence of which our brains are not *as yet* programmed to comprehend and, if so, what sort of time do *they* keep? We hear talk of the 'real world', but what is that 'real world'? Is it only real because of its perceptibility to our physical senses and our left-brain logic? Within the world of psychology it is acknowledged that one person's 'reality' is not necessarily another's, so can the same principle be applied to the cosmos?

Paul Davies is among those scientists who see fit to keep an open mind as to what we might discover as 'Lady Scientia' slowly discards her veils. He comments:

Because scientists have revealed, and believe in, laws of nature, they accept that the universe 'ticks over' on its own, unaided by, and oblivious of, our own involvement in it. The obviousness of this is all the more striking when we discover how ill-founded it is.

24

Clearly the world that a person actually experiences cannot be totally objective, because we experience the world by interacting with it . . .

The purpose of physical science has been to disengage from this personalized and semi-subjective view of the world and to build a model of reality which is *independent* of the observer. Traditional procedures to attain this goal are repeatable experiments, measurement by machine, mathematical formulation, etc. How successful is this objective model provided by science? Can it actually describe a world which exists independently of the people who perceive it?[1]

The Anthropic Principle

The 'reality' which we perceive, and which is confirmed by many branches of science, consists of a picture of the material universe which is based on observation, equation and experiment. Hawking comments: 'We see the universe the way it is because we exist.'[2] This forms the basis of what is known as the 'anthropic principle', which defines that from an infinite number of possibilities nature could have selected to make a universe, it chose this one so that we could be created. There are two versions of this principle, the weak and the strong, depending on which interpretation of the quantum theory is adopted. Coveney and Highfield also mention a 'final anthropic principle', which maintains in addition that 'once life has come into existence in the universe, it will never die out.'[3] The weak anthropic principle (proposed by Brandon Carter in 1973), which accords with the conventional Copenhagen Interpretation (see Glossary) states that only our world really exists – we are here because the conditions are right, and conversely the conditions are right because we are here! The strong anthropic principle contends that the universe must be such as to allow the existence of life, and is often used as the way out of the uncomfortable conclusions of the weak version.

However, scientists appear to disagree among themselves regarding the conventionally accepted anthropic principle. Lederman and Schramm, for example, who recently postulated a connection between the immense scale of the universe and the unimaginably tiny microworld inside the atom – the dramatic merger of physics and cosmology, showing how experiments and theoretical predictions developed in one area provide clues and solutions to problems in the other – and how these converging fields may soon produce as 'theory of everything'. I quote:

So far we've discussed our ultimate goal as a single theory of everything, which will be unique – the only theory to be mathematically consistent. Some respectable scientists have taken a somewhat different approach. They have argued that instead of searching for a unique, mathematically consistent theory, the properties of our universe are governed instead by 'the anthropic principle'. This principle asserts that the laws of physics are what they are because they are the only ones that can produce intelligent beings (us?) who can contemplate the universe. For this principle, the only universes that count are those that ultimately evolve beings who can contemplate them.

Followers of the anthropic principle argue that a huge number of universes might exist with very different physical laws, but the laws in our universe are the only ones that enable intelligent beings to exist. Such a principle is one way to avoid worrying about finding a unique, mathematically consistent theory. Instead we might assume that there exists a plethora of mathematically consistent theories, but most don't yield people and are no fun. Although there have been entire books written on the anthropic principle (e.g. J. Barrow and F. Tipler's *The Anthropic Principle* Oxford University Press, 1986) we really don't see it as useful. In our opinion it is a way to avoid answering questions ('things are as they are because they were as they were'), rather than a principle that has led to a new understanding.[4]

This view is also shared by Fred Hoyle, who referred to the anthropic principle as 'a modern attempt to evade all implications of purpose in the universe, no matter how remarkable our environment turns out to be.' He also commented, 'The logic of the anthropic principle is rather like that in a famous paradox put forward by the mathematician Bertrand Russell: "In a town it is the practice of the town barber to shave everybody who does not shave themselves." Now although this statement, like the anthropic principle, sounds innocent enough, it is actually loaded with contradiction . . .'[5]

It would seem logical to assume that in a universe that is unlimited by space-time, intelligent life will only develop in those regions that have space-time limitations. Intelligent beings in those regions will thus be inclined to see the conditions prevalent within their locality as necessary for their existence, while ignoring the fact that other cosmic neighbourhoods may well be thinking the same of the requirements appropriate to their evolution. The weak anthropic principle, therefore, appeals to many on egotistical grounds, on the one hand, and taking into account what might be seen as the logical sequences of cosmic evolution, on the other. Cosmologists do not agree among themselves as to what constitutes the ingredients essential to the development of 'intelligent life', but then it would seem that many of them are basing their idea of intelligence on the *Homo sapiens* model. However, this is hardly surprising in view of the attitudes towards other life forms adopted by the major world religions. Also, although many men and women of science claim to be total atheists, the subconscious worship of their own tribal/ancestral deities, and their exalted view of their species as a whole, would appear to influence their judgement rather more than they might care to admit. After all, do we appear in our present hominid form by sheer coincidence, or was our particular species specially designed by some transcendent force to accommodate a superior manifestation of intelligent life?

In his book *Cosmos*, Carl Sagan wrote:

> Were the Earth to be started over again with all its physical features identical, it is extremely unlikely that anything closely resembling a human being would ever again emerge. There is a powerful random character to the evolutionary process. A cosmic ray striking a different gene, producing a different mutation, can have small consequences early, but profound consequences late. Happenstance may play a powerful role in biology, as it does in history. The farther back the critical events occur, the more powerfully they can influence the present.[6]

Bearing in mind this and similar views held by other scientists, we have no guarantee that the hominid form is the most advanced evolutionary model in the material universe. Paul Davies, for example, points out the fact that crystals are highly organized structures capable of reproducing themselves, and stars are complex and elaborately organized systems, while Fred Hoyle conceives of living clouds of cosmic matter that are self-motivated and control their own motion much like an amoeba. Are all these things not 'living' and 'intelligent'? Taking all this into account, plus James Lovelock's view that the Earth is an autonomous, self-regulating entity in her own right, surely places a different slant on the myth of the supremacy of man.

Several objections to the strong anthropic principle have surfaced from various scientific disciplines, one of which questions the validity of any system which claims that the observable universe exists simply for our sake. The issues involved are highly complex, however, and those readers wishing for further detail are referred to the Bibliography. Our prime concern as regards the universe generally, and our own neck of the cosmic woods in particular, is that of Time, which brings us around to the inevitable question of the Big Bang and its predicted demise, the Big Crunch, was it or was it not?

The Big Bang

The physics and chemistry of the Big Bang theory have been well and truly chewed over by cosmologists, so all that is left for me is to comment on what I see as the illogical aspects of this hypothesis. Hawking points out that since we are only in possession of the knowledge of what has happened *since* the Big Bang, we have no way of determining what took place before then, and should therefore accept that time as we know it began with our noisy friend. Many people reject the Big Bang or 'singularity' theory on the grounds that it suggests some divine intervention, several orthodox religions having seized upon it to substantiate their belief in the biblical creation myth. To follow the idea through to its logical conclusion suggests an expanding universe, time being counted from its commencement, which will eventually collapse on itself – the Big Crunch!

The apocalyptic prophecies of the German physicist Hermann von Helmholtz in 1854, which dealt with the eventual demise of the universe, were based on the Second Law of Thermodynamics. The remorseless rise in entropy that accompanies any natural process could, he felt, lead only to the final cessation of all life-giving activity throughout the universe. Helmholtz envisioned a slowly dying universe, inexorably squandering its finite and irretrievable resources, and so choking on its own entropy.

What puzzles me about all this is that since waves appear to play such an important role in the cosmos, why has the wave principle not been applied to the life cycle of the universe? For example, let us suppose that our universe responds to a rhythm of expansion and contraction according to some presently incalculable or inconceivable law of periodicity, a variation of frequencies occurring with each 'exhalation and inhalation', no experience ever being repeated, in which case it would never approach absolute expansion or contraction but move through a central constant. And besides, as I have previously contended, what proof do we have that what *we* see as the physical universe is, in fact, the only one?

Since astronomy is one of the few physical sciences to which amateurs can make valuable contributions and discoveries alongside the professionals, I discussed my idea with American amateur astronomer Jared Collard, who offered the following hypothesis:

THE NON-SINGULARITY THEORY
The oft-hypothesized Big Bang theory proposes that the universe, or the space-time continuum, began at some given moment in time in the past, originating from a state of singularity [a hypothetical point

in space at which matter is infinitely compressed to infinitesimal volume], and that given sufficient mass the universe will collapse back upon itself at some time in the future and return once more to singularity. Visually this could be represented thus:

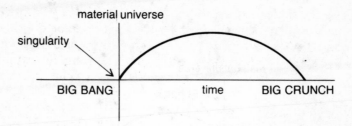

In mathematics this is referred to as a sine curve. However, this curve is incomplete for it implies that when all matter once again returns to singularity everything stops! In other words, is the universe a one-time miracle or does it rebound once more from singularity, skipping through time like a flat stone over a pond?

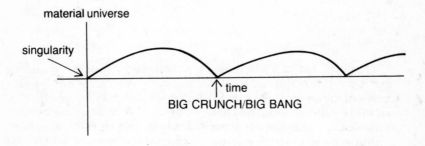

Surely this curve represents only *half* of a complete sine wave?

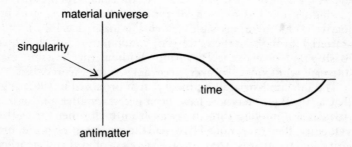

Or is it a series of interconnecting sine waves?

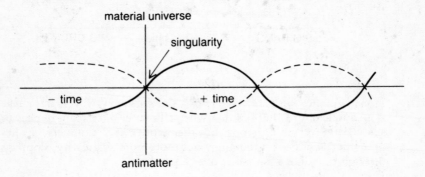

The portion of the wave above the time line is positive matter and the portion below is antimatter. If this sine wave is an accurate representation of the cosmos, the paradox is that we cannot know whether we are in the matter or antimatter universe or whether, in fact, these two universes exist simultaneously separated only by a thin membrane of time.

Astrophysicists are frantically looking for the 'missing matter', the all-important enigmatic mass necessary to provide sufficient gravity not only to slow down and eventually halt the expansion of the universe, but also cause it to reverse its course and bring it back once more to singularity. So far they have succeeded in locating only 10 per cent of the mass they believe is necessary to initiate the collapse of the universe back to singularity. The missing 90 per cent, they believe, may be 'dark matter' – unknown, invisible elements or mass particles which may be scattered throughout the space-time continuum in sufficient quantities to stop and reverse the expansion. Without this 'missing mass' the universe will expand forever, according to the theoreticians.

The Lifshitz Khalatnikov theory, first proposed in 1963, suggested that a Big Bang may not have been necessary after all. Since not all galaxies are moving directly away from each other, or at the same velocities, they must not all have had the same starting point, or singularity (unless, that is, some proto-galaxies collided and ricocheted off one another at some point soon after the Big Bang; not a very realistic possibility). These two Russians originally hypothesized that the universe may have natural contraction and expansion phases, and therefore no singularity was required. It's unfortunate that Lifshitz and Khalatnikov repudiated their own theory in 1970 and accepted the Friedmann models that singularity did probably occur. However, their original hypothesis could be supported by the Pauli Exclusion Principle if it is applied to a cosmic scale, and not merely limited in its scope to explaining why some stars suffer an internal collapse when their nuclear fuels have been exhausted and others do not.

In 1928, an Indian graduate student, Subrahmanyan Chandrasekhar, worked out how large a star could be and still support itself against the force of its own gravity after its nuclear fuel had been exhausted. 'When a star becomes small, the matter particles get very near each other, and so according to the Pauli Exclusion Principle, they must have very different velocities. This makes them move away from each other and so tends to make the star expand. A star can therefore maintain itself at a constant radius by a balance between the attraction of gravity and the repulsion that arises from the exclusion principle, just as earlier in its life gravity was balanced by heat.[7] It has been observed that our sun slightly expands and contracts at fairly regular intervals due to the fluctuations in the delicate balance between the forces of nuclear fusion from hydrogen to helium and gravitational attraction – almost like a breathing in and a breathing out, according to metaphysical belief. If this is so, the sine curve might look like this:

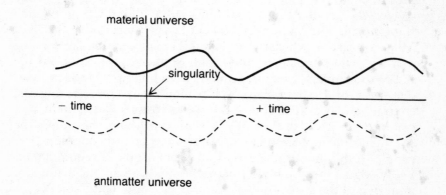

Pauli's Exclusion Principle should apply to the entire cosmos. That the most distant galaxies have a higher rate of recessional speed has been observed and measured. During a contraction phase they would continue to have a different rate of speed, thereby presumably creating the necessary counterforce to the contraction and preventing a return to singularity. Moreover, aside from the velocity problem there is another consideration. Since, presumably, not all galaxies are the same distance from wherever the original starting point was, they cannot all return to singularity at the same time, thereby preventing the universe from returning to singularity since its mass would be neither complete nor infinite until all mass has been accounted for.

The underlying inference here would appear to be that time did not commence with the supposed Big Bang, since there never was one, but that the universe is an infinite Intelligence that exists in a state of perpetual timelessness, its thought patterns manifesting in an infinite range of frequencies from the incomprehensible to the more familiar worlds of matter. Those intelligences that inhabit what we would refer to as the 'physical' universe would naturally view their surroundings in the solid context simply because they exist within the same waveband! I wonder how many of my readers will have undergone the experience of being 'out of the body', either in sleep state or while undergoing some transpersonal experience, and found to their annoyance that the light switch refused to work, or the handles of the doors respond to being turned? But upon waking – returning to the frequency of the material dimension – all these things are seen to function perfectly.

The Lifshitz/Khalatnikov theory[8] and its retraction admitted, there is nothing new in the idea of a living universe, the exhaled breath of which probably gave birth to the Big Bang, while conversely its inhalations could be read as the much prophesied Big Crunch. The Metternich Stele of Egypt refers to the 'Boat of a Million Years' in which the Sun God Ra makes his regular celestial journey, while Indian scientific philosophers have estimated the age of the universe as approximately two billion years. However, the 'Year of Brahma' lasts 321 trillion years, representing the contraction and expansion of the entire cosmos. The Hindu year count refers to a cycle, each 'cosmic breathing' heralding the commencement of another cycle of trillions of years duration. The people from whom these early Indian philosophers acquired their knowledge must obviously have been aware of the nature of infinity and the space-time curvature. (See also The Vedic Yugas in Chapter 5.)

A Cosmic Brain?

Interestingly enough, a team of four scientists, using powerful optical telescopes in Australia and the USA, has recently completed the first survey of 200 galaxies in a 'slice' of the universe over six billion light years across. During their seven-year project they discovered that galaxies were evenly distributed in 'clumps', each of which were about 400 million light years apart. This has led them to believe that the universe may be a giant 'honeycomb' of regular, repeating, galactic cells with each cell diameter as large as 300–400 million light years. The team, which included Richard Ellis, Professor of Astronomy at Durham University, and Dr Tom Broadhurst of Queen Mary and Westfield College, London, intends to carry out further studies to try to gain a greater grasp of the implications. Richard Ellis was interviewed by Nigel Williams of the *Observer*, (23 March 1990), in which the question arose as to how the results of this study affected the reliability of the redshift (see Glossary) as a measure of distance. Ellis told him:

> There's now very good evidence from quasars. Quasars have been seen behind objects of lower redshift and when light from a distant object passes the gas clouds of a foreground object, a certain feature in the spectrum is produced showing unambiguously that object A is behind object B. And in every case where that has been tested, the higher the redshift the more distant the object. But that isn't to say that occasionally, in exotic parts of the universe, there are other contributions to redshift. But for regular objects like galaxies the correlation, I think, is now watertight.

One of the bizarre things to emerge from the theoretical attempts to explain the clumpiness of galactic structure is the notion of 'dark matter'. (See also Chapter 3.) Known only by its gravitational effects on visible galaxies, it is thought to make up as much as 90 per cent of mass of the universe and be the hidden force behind cosmic order.

Anyone reading the aforegoing could not fail to be struck by the similarity between these universal 'honeycombs' and the cellular construction of the human brain, which is surely nothing more than a complex computer that is programmed in much the same way as any other similar instrument. Is the universe, therefore, a giant brain that contains elements of both order *and* chaos, which would appear to be essential prerequisites to any intelligence with an infinite capacity for both knowledge *and* understanding, since one is not synonymous with the other? Which brings us round to the thorny subject of religion.

I find the idea of a single deity, conceived of in human terms (e.g. 'the image and likeness of man') as being tribal, parochial and limited by any standards of logic, universal or otherwise. But is there really a single ghost in this great cosmic machine? I rather think not. If we must have such things neatly pigeonholed I would suggest that the ancient Egyptians probably had the right idea when they viewed the Intelligence behind all creation as having many faces. After all, who are we that from among the infinity of the cosmos, the Mind behind it all should elect to take on our human appearance? Fortunately, we are now entering an era in which many of these obsolete, tribal ideas will go by the board and the reality of our equality with *all* the other life forms with which we share this planet will be forced upon us by a series of catastrophic and tragic circumstances. But more of that later when we come to discuss other cycles of periodicity.

Which bring us back to the question of time. Assuming there are other universes, the odds against any of their inhabitants sharing the same concept of time as our own would be remote, to say the least. In fact, it has often been postulated that these universes, be they parallel or otherwise, exist within each other, albeit at different frequencies, so that we cannot see them, in much the same way that we cannot see X-rays, gamma rays, radio waves, or electrical current. Of course, it can be argued that these energies are there because we have detected their presence and invented instruments that can both measure them and utlilize them for our own convenience. My answer to that one is this: a few hundred years ago such phenomena would have been classified as 'occult' 'witchcraft', 'magic' or similar, and it is only because we now have the technology with which to observe and harness them that they have assumed respectable proportions. Exactly the same applies to parallel universes, psi phenomena, and similar wavebands at present imperceptible to even the finest instruments, which may eventually be found to obey a somewhat different set of scientific laws than those of which we are presently aware. Into this category falls our enigmatic friend time, which I believe to be the connecting link between all energy fields, both perceptible and imperceptible.

Order versus Chaos

According to accepted laws of physics, the cosmos, as we perceive it, obeys an established set of rules. In other words, it could be classified as 'organized', since it appears to be moving in a curve-like path through the orderly towards the chaotic, or from the Big Bang to the Big Crunch. However, it would seem that not all universes conform to this pattern of orderliness, there being those in which disorder reigns throughout, and others that commence in a disorderly state and progress towards order. Paul Davies submits that in such worlds time would run 'backwards' relative to our own world and, were they to be inhabited by observers, he supposes that their brains would also be subject to the reverse operation so that, other than regarding it as contracting rather than expanding, their perception of the universe would differ little from our own. Surely this is suggestive of the Collard graphs (see pages 28–31) which illustrate the continuing cycles of the universe – while one cosmic frequency is experiencing the inhalation, the other is simultaneously experiencing the exhalation!

Davies suggests that the connection between our own existence, the asymmetry in time of the world around us, and the initial cosmic order should be viewed in the context of superspace. He tells us:

> When the equations for the quantum development of superspace are examined, they are found to be reversible – they do not distinguish past from future. In superspace there is no distinct past and future. Some of the worlds certainly have a strong past-future property and these are precisely the ones that can support life. Others have a future-past, reversed, asymmetry and presumably are also inhabited. The vast majority, however, have no such peculiar distinction between past and future, so are quite unsuitable for life and go unnoticed. In the Everett theory all these other worlds, including the reversed-time ones, really exist alongside us. In the more conventional theory they are possible worlds which, by incredible good fortune, did not come to exist, though they could still exist in the remote future or on the other side of the universe. It could be that our own cosy, highly ordered world is just a local bubble of equability in a predominantly chaotic cosmos, seen by us only because our very existence depends on the benign conditions here.[9]

Are there different worlds existing in different time 'zones', some of which are in the future according to our concept of time: is this difficult to compute? Not really. I share the belief with many psychologists that we dream 'out of time'. Frequently in those parallel universes fragments of our 'essence' may indeed be experiencing what to them are very physical and real conditions. And since in Outer Time there is a point at which all time is one, it is only the 'orderliness' of Inner Time that brings us down to what we perceive as earthly reality. Equally, intelligent beings from future worlds as yet uncreated, according to our time frame, may well have surpassed us in technological and mental achievement, and therefore able to 'look back' into our worlds with interest and fascination. Telepathy from the future? And why not. Where do the ideas come from that have revolutionized our thinking, science and technology over the past centuries? A study of dreams will tell us just how many scientists have 'seen' their inventions in a dream or visited a parallel universe that exists in our past or future, in which intelligent life has already effected these developments, wherein they have observed them, and awakened to bestow yet another gift of knowledge upon a waiting world. But more of this later.

A 'Jigsaw' Theory?

The evolutionary cycle of a planet such as Earth, or even the solar system which it occupies, could be conceived of in terms of a giant jigsaw, the original picture of which has been created at some other point in superspace where all time is one, but which has subsequently shattered upon impact with a denser or lower frequency. Therefore, at the beginning of the 'time' that Hawking and his fellow scientists would associate with the Big Bang, the pieces are all jumbled up in a chaotic heap. Then slowly, the moving Hand of Time carefully reassembles them until the picture is once again complete and order reigns for a period, until the materials of which it is constructed, through the stress of time, begin to experience 'time fatigue' (entropy?). In other words, they wear out and the downward spiral to chaos commences. But during the interval that the picture has been complete, it will have become imprinted on, or programmed into, the minds of many of the life forms that have existed during its period of order. And since the mind, psyche, or 'essence' is itself a quantum factor (see Chapter 8), intelligences from the old world who are born into new worlds will slowly unfold their knowledge through dreams of their past collective unconscious to contribute to the birth, growth and development of the next cycle. And so the pieces of the jigsaw will once again be reassembled, but this time the picture will be slightly different, as it will be coloured by the vision of its reality as experienced by those who formerly beheld it; and as we all know, ten people looking at a picture may each view it and interpret its message in a different context.

Superspace

The term 'superspace' has been coined to define an imaginary mathematical structure which envisions situations in which there exist more than three dimensions. The concept was created by physicists who were attempting to effect a uniting point between relativity and quantum physics. Superspace contains points in much the same way as ordinary space does, only each point in superspace marks the location of every object in a whole universe. In other words, each point in superspace is a scale model of a whole and distinct universe.

Like the underworld of myth and legend, the world of quantum physics is one of chaos. Continual subatomic transmutations effect random changes, endowing the whole process with a chance-like quality. In this strange, dark and unpredictable region, the undisciplined particles of matter proceed about their chaotic business unaware, perhaps, of the essential nature of their role in the cosmic scheme of things. The backcloth against which this scenario is acted out is, of course, that of superspace. Equally, space-time itself is now known to possess dynamic qualities which cause it to curve, mutate, or act with the unpredictability assigned to it by Chaos Science. Changes in space and time can therefore occur on or around the Earth itself, or way out in the universe. In other words, the predictability factor is by no means as hard and fast as science might at one time have had us believe.

I am reminded of a science programme shown on television some years ago when the viewers were treated to a close-up of a chaotic jumble of life-cells that were in the early process of dividing. The camera lens was then adjusted to encompass a distant, more overall view, whereupon that which had formerly appeared as haphazard and confused assumed a symmetry of great beauty.

May we gather from this small, and perhaps insignificant, fact that the disorderliness and unpredictability of the quantum worlds eventually give way to the order of those more solid states that appear to obey so rigidly the old Newtonian laws? Or, better still, is that secure rigidity that has formed the basis of science for so many years simply another of those phases in the waves of evolution, and the security of this supposed solidity will eventually give way to entropy and disengage its structures in readiness for its eventual change into another form or dimension of energy? After all, according to Chaos Science chaos is eventually self-organizing, so why not the reverse, in a continuing cycle? And what is the deciding factor in all of these changes? Time. Viewed as an energy, perhaps time could be seen as a spiralling rather than linear wave of infinite length, along which the phases and amplitudes of our own, and all other universes, proceed?

In commenting on superspace, Paul Davies draws our attention to the possibility that gravity, one of the prime forces in the universe, might possibly function on the 'wave' principle, gravity waves being visualized as undulations of space, radiating away from a source of disturbance.[10] In fact, according to a report in the *Guardian* (12 October, 1990) a German-British team is vying to be the first to detect gravitational waves. Now that most of the electromagnetic spectrum is open to astronomy, there is apparently a race on to exploit gravitational radiation. Professor Jim Hough, of the University of Glasgow, and Dr Karsten Danzmann, of the Max Planck Institute for Quantum Optics at Garching, near Munich, are the principal partners in the venture to build the world's first gravitational wave observatory. Although Einstein's theory of relativity predicts that waves should be generated wherever masses are accelerated, they are apparently so weak that they could only be detected from violent events on a cosmic scale. This is interesting in the light of my earlier remarks concerning waves. The likelihood of the wave as a universal constant therefore merits serious consideration.

The acknowledged duality of relativity and quantum physics, as viewed in the order/chaos context, did not appear to pose a problem for past students of the universe, however, although in those distant times those following the path of scientific discovery tended to be somewhat more open-minded when it came to matters metaphysical. After all, Newton himself was a fervent believer in astrology and his famous comment to the doubting Halley, of comet fame: 'Sir, I have studied it, you have not!' has been cited in defence of the subject since Newton first uttered it *c.* 1680.

The Ouroboros Theory

There are other ideas regarding the evolution of the universe that border on the metaphysical and are therefore shunned by orthodox science; the ouroboros theory, for example, and the spiral concept to which it is closely related. The former of these conceives of a universal evolutionary cycle that commences at the position of the 'serpent's head', which represents the chaos immediately following birth, proceeds through the lower curve of stability to return once again to the chaotic mode. Upon reaching this point, instead of effecting an exact repetition of the previous circle it varies its frequency, albeit slightly, before engaging in the circular (or spiral?) repeat. In this way no experience is ever

duplicated or replayed exactly. The only difference between this and the parallel universe theory would appear to be the linear/non-linear time factors, or Inner and Outer Time.

There is an interesting corollary here from the world of psychology. The Spanish psychologist and philosopher J. E. Cirlot, writing on the subject of the ouroboros, tells us:

> This symbol appears principally among the Gnostics and is depicted as a dragon, snake or serpent biting its own tail. In the broadest sense, it is symbolic of time and of the continuity of life. It sometimes bears the caption *Hen to pan* – 'The One, the All', as in the *Codex Marcianus*, for instance, of the 2nd century A.D. It has also been explained as the union between the chthonian [underworld] principle as represented by the serpent and the celestial principle as signified by the bird (a synthesis which can also be applied to the dragon). Ruland contends that this proves that it is a variant of the symbol for Mercury – the *duplex* god. In some versions of the Ouroboros, the body is half light and half dark, alluding in this way to the successive counterbalancing of opposing principles as illustrated in the Chinese *Yang-Yin* symbol for instance. Evola asserts that it represents the dissolution of the body, or the universal serpent which (to quote the Gnostic saying) 'passes through all things'. Poison, the viper and the universal solvent are all symbols of the undifferentiated – of the 'unchanging law' which moves through all things, linking them by a common bond. . . The ouroboros biting its own tail is symbolic of self-fecundation, or the primitive idea of a self-sufficient Nature – a Nature, that is, which, *à la* Nietzsche, continually returns, within a cyclic pattern, to its own beginning.[11]

Since the ouroboros was one of the prime symbols of that forerunner of modern chemistry – alchemy – one must assume that the scholars of past ages had some idea of the structure and movement of the universe in principle, even if they lacked the technology to substantiate their theories. One must also remember that in ancient times principles were often represented by mythical personalities to whom certain attributes were ascribed that could be both easily understood by the unlettered, and serve as adequate terms of reference to the lettered. Hermes, Mercury, Thoth, Sîn, Aion, all gods of time, were inevitably dual-aspected and fast moving. They ruled over the chthonic regions (the world of chaotic subatomic transmutation) on the one hand, and were also capable of travelling from one heaven to another, galaxy to galaxy. Does this sound familiar?

Space-times

The term 'space-time' is frequently used in contemporary studies and dissertations on the subject of cosmology. For example, there is the space-time arena, curved space-time, flat space-time, and quantum space-time.

'Space-time arena' refers to the vast volume of all the space in the universe and all time *as known and understood at present*. Each point in space-time is registered as an event that is marked by both its spatial coordinates and its temporal coordinate. Since our perception of the space-time arena is continually expanding, however, so is this arena and one could speculate that in time it will include other, more subtle universes that will eventually be detected and charted as technology advances.

Curved space-time is based on the notion that all of space and time together make up a four-dimensional surface that is curved in some way. The American theoretical physicist, Fred Alan Wolf, gives us the following example to explain this curve:

> Imagine a global sphere. Lines of longitude represent time, and lines of latitude represent space. By moving along a line of longitude one passes through the poles. A journey northward after passing through the north pole takes one southward. A north-bound journey is a passage forward in time while the southward journey takes one backward through time. [12]

According to 'flat space-time' all of space and time together make up a four-dimensional, flat surface. Applying Wolf's previous example to this concept one could view it as a sheet of paper upon which both horizontal and vertical lines are drawn. The horizontal lines represent space, and the vertical lines time. In all these proposals it may be observed that, once again, time plays a crucial and undeniable part.

Quantum space-time, on the other hand, is seen as inhabiting a world more remote in its smallness than the ends of the universe would appear in their incalculable immensity. But, in spite of this, energies set in motion within the supposed chaos of the quantum world of minute particles can have repercussions at all levels of the cosmos. If we look at the overall picture of the space-times, we will perceive that they are by no means uniform and featureless, but a complex and ever-changing labyrinth of perpetual motion.

Davies asserts that time does not *pass*, nor is there a past, present and future as such. It is we, and every other life form within the cosmos – every particle, from the minutest as yet undiscovered to the largest object we are at present able to view, and those even larger beyond, that effect the movement. And it is that movement which, as I see it, employs the energy of time, that causes our universe and other, less perceptible worlds, to tick over. But what of timelessness or Outer Time? Timelessness exists within all time and is embraced within the Outer Time concept, Outer Time being simply a convenient term of reference for those time-zones that do not form part of the time structure with which we are familiar on Earth.

When I was a small child at boarding school we were told that God was everywhere, and therefore always watching us wherever we were or whatever we did. I recall this causing me some initial consternation, especially when attending to the normal, daily bodily requirements. Eventually, I dismissed the matter by rationalizing that if this great Being had really created me, he, she, or it must have had a hand at designing my anatomy and physiology, and as such would expect things to work according to plan. Later in life I realized that what they were really explaining to me, although I doubt whether they themselves were aware of the fact, was that there were other worlds existing simultaneously with our own at different frequencies, imperceptible to the physical senses, and any intelligence sufficiently sensitive to negotiate these would be able to observe both my private personal habits and those of every other living creature.

I seem to recall there being a passage in the Bible to the effect that not a sparrow falls without God being aware of it. In my language the most fleeting movement and communication of the tiniest particle is registered in Outer Time, *simultaneously with every other movement and thought, at every point of time conceivable or computable by our brains in their present stage of development, and beyond*. It is only our isolation in this time-zone we call the present that obscures our view of Outer Time which is, perhaps, for the best as far as many people are concerned. Outer Time consciousness can be mind. blowing if the brain is not programmed to handle it – until the next quantum leap, that is!

Time and Light

It was not so long ago that scientists shared the common belief that nothing could exceed the speed of light, and physicists had a heyday speculating as to what would happen if a rocket were to reach the speed of light, its front portion arriving at that point fractionally earlier than its rear portion, and how this would appear to the observer. However, today even this is debatable. Scientists are now able to investigate with great precision the behaviour of single atoms in different energy states, how atoms 'jump' from one state to another, and how the invisible probabilistic world of the particle becomes expressed in forms that can be easily understood in the more solid world of our own reality. Electronics and astrophysics, it would seem, are rapidly moving into a new era which exploits zero signal times and embraces the mysterious possibility of communicating instantly across extensive ranges. Biochemist Dr Rupert Sheldrake reiterated this belief in his theory of morphic resonance, in which he postulated that particles are able to communicate with each other instantaneously over vast distances.

When one considers that the human, and other minds or intelligences, have been achieving just this over the centuries, it does seem rather strange that there should be so much excitement at the prospect of a technology producing similar results. Perhaps it is the possibility of eliminating that old 'probability' bogey that has dominated the world of parapsychology and metaphysics for so many years that is proving the proverbial carrot for this particular donkey! Time will tell. The observation of minute quantum leaps does interest me, however. Working on the assumption that these miniscule patterns are repetitive in the wave frequencies of larger objects (the macrocosm/microcosm principle) might help ecologists and climatologists, in particular, to assess the possibility of any forthcoming quantum leaps that could affect drastically our weather patterns on Earth on the one hand, and any impending evolutionary mutations that could change the life cycles of Gaia's 'children' on the other. Also, one cannot help wondering whether it was some form of quantum leap that transported the observable universe through the Big Bang phase, and will eventually hasten it through the Big Crunch (via the agency of entropy, or antimatter?) to its next state, whatever that may be; but *be*, I am convinced, it *will!*

Quantum Leaps

Orthodox science defines quantum leaps, or jumps, as the transition of an atomic or molecular system from one discrete energy level to another, which process normally occurs with absorption or emission of radiation having energy equal to the difference between the two levels. The term is also used to designate a major breakthrough or sudden advance. However, as I, and certain other researchers and philosophers see it, quantum leaps can occur in every area of life and experience from the interplay of minute particles to the evolution of consciousness. Their effect upon Earth in the distant past has often been denied by those scientists who have staunchly supported the old 'solid state' theory, but fortunately a combination of quantum physics and Chaos Science is in the process of exorcizing that old spook once and for all. Does the universe itself experience quantum jumps from time to time? Physicists cannot say for sure that it does, although the Copenhagen interpretation would appear to suggest the likelihood, based on the behaviour of particles in quantum, plus the probability factor.

Quantum jumps could be seen to represent accelerated points in the flow of time's energy. Imagine that you are being driven along a motorway in a medium-sized car at a steady 70 miles per hour. The journey so far has gone smoothly, there is little traffic about, your driver is conscientious and thoroughly reliable, and you find yourself lulled into a false sense of security. Suddenly, out of the blue, a large vehicle travelling *in the opposite lane* careers out of control and crosses the central reserve. Your driver is quick to take evasive action; he swings his vehicle round at right angles, accelerating hard to avoid the oncoming truck, crosses the reserve in the process, but eventually manages, with great skill to restore it to its previous steady line and pace – *only you are now proceeding in the opposite direction!* Sometimes, however, our hypothetical driver may be unable to avoid the obstruction that has suddenly appeared across his or her pathway, and disaster ensues. It would seem that unless one has some special, telepathic form of communication with those worlds that normally exist outside the stream of human consciousness one may be caught unawares, like the dinosaurs and later the mammoths of Siberia. Myth and legend is strewn with such instances, only we are now having to face the frightening truth that these were not all the fairy-tales we might previously have believed, they were quantum leap realities, and the likelihood of their occurring again, in our lifetimes, looms threateningly in the immediately future.

Endnotes

1. P. Davies, *Other Worlds*, p. 108.
2. S. W. Hawking, *A Brief History of Time*, p. 124.
3. P. Coveney, and R. Highfield, *The Arrow of Time*, p. 103.
4. L. M. Lederman and D. M. Schramm, *From Quarks to Cosmos*, p. 229.
5. F. Hoyle, *The Intelligent Universe*, p. 220.
6. C. Sagan, *Cosmos* , p. 282.
7. S. W. Hawking, *A Brief History of Time*, p. 83.
8. *Ibid*. pp. 48–9.
9. P. Davies, *Other Worlds* pp. 198–9.
10. *Ibid*. p. 93.
11. C. E. Cirlot, *A Dictionary of Symbols*, p. 235.
12. F. A. Wolf, *Parallel Universes*, pp. 328–9.

3
Parallel Universes?

Time has but one reality, that of the instant. In other words, time is a reality confined to the instant and suspended between two worlds.
GASTON BACHELARD

Many theories have been propounded by both theoretical physicists and science fiction writers regarding the possibility of a series of parallel universes coexisting side by side with our own, albeit on different dimensions or at different frequencies which render them imperceptible to each other. It has even been speculated that there could be worlds where the whole process of time is reversed so that a lifespan would commence at what we see as the point of death, and progress backwards to the womb; events would appear rather like a film in reverse where water disappears back into the tap, a fallen building reassembles itself, and so forth. This sounds all very strange according to our understanding, and one cannot help but feel rather more secure behind the tensed bowstring of Eddington's famous arrow.

Energized Circuits of Time?

But why should a parallel universe necessarily involve the reversal of the forward-time procedure? The answer must be that it does not, but rather that backward time, if such a thing does exist, functions within some subtle dimension that does not involve matter as we know it but which will eventually be recognized as one of time's hidden dimensions. What I am suggesting is that there are frequencies of time with which we are as yet unfamiliar, although we may speculate as to their existence, and when we do finally locate them we will find that they are negotiable outside what we accept as the physical world. No, I am not referring to some vague, metaphysical concept, but to a not yet discovered

45

and uncharted energy field which interpenetrates all dimensions, including those that our present technology is as yet incapable of registering. This field is a kind of multi-directional grid that could be likened to the complex circuitry of a super-computer whose terminals are linked to both the past and future. And, being a source of energy in itself, once identified and understood it could enable its negotiators to move through time, and the universe, at will.

Correspondingly, we could view it as a nexus of motorways, the exits of which exist at specific intervals, each of which points in a different direction – forwards or backwards in our own universe, sideways towards another parallel physical world, or into some inconceivable dimension of the 'Star Trek' or 'Dr Who' variety. Future time travellers would therefore need to be skilled readers of these road signs, or they could find themselves facing in the wrong direction, or having to double back to the last exit – all very *time*-consuming! These points of egress could possibly be equated with time warps or time slips, depending on the specific nature of their energies in quantum terms. Another analogy would be a railway network with its various dropping-off points or 'cosmic stations', only there would be no trains as such, since the traveller would provide his or her own vehicle. It would simply be a matter of plugging into some energy-carrying rail or overhead power cable, in much the same way that an electric train effects its connection with the power, and away you would go. Sci-fi? Don't you believe it! It *is* there, and it is destined to play an important role in the science of our future.

The Parallel Universe theme first found favour with physicists during the 1950s and 60s, appearing as a revolutionary way of making concrete sense of the bizarre findings of quantum physics and general relativity. However, such visions demand a revised concept of reality, and the paradoxes confronting science are still too vague and ill-defined to necessitate any radical departure from the physics of Newton and Einstein that have proved so accurate, as far as our space probes are concerned.

In essence, the Parallel Universe theory postulates the existence of an infinite number of universes, many of which bear a similarity to the one with which we are familiar, wherein matter exists in parallel to our own world, and in which we might also have a *doppelgänger* or ghostly counterpart. However, the twin-soul concept is nothing new, having appeared in various esoteric teachings down the ages. The American theoretical physicist Fred Alan Wolf assures us:

Not only in a parallel universe must there be other human beings, but these may be human beings who are exact duplicates of ourselves and who are connected to ourselves through mechanisms explainable only by using quantum physics concepts.[1]

Wolf also sees the existence of parallel universes as leading towards a unification of new ideas about the familiar universe: quantum physics, relativity, cosmology, a new notion of time, and psychology. He foresees a future in which suitably programmed and highly complex computers, working in Outer Time, could help us to effect decisions in our everyday lives, based on knowledge of possible future outcomes and the lessons learned in parallel existences. However, he is careful to point out that:

> The laboratory of parallel universe experimentation may not lie in a mechanical time machine à la Jules Verne, but could exist between our ears.
>
> If the parallel universes of relativity are the same as those of the quantum theory the possibility exists that parallel universes may be extremely close to us, perhaps only atomic dimensions away but perhaps in a higher dimension of space – an extension into what physicists call *superspace*. Modern neuroscience, through the study of altered states of awareness, schizophrenia, and lucid dreaming, could be indicating the closeness of parallel worlds to our own.[2]

In this latter statement I find myself in total agreement with Dr Wolf, and in later chapters I hope to provide evidence of how our experiences in alternative worlds complement and help us through the switchback ride that constitutes our present reality. The mind is, indeed, the precursor of the inter-space computer and will eventually replace it once mankind has cottoned onto the fact that it can do anything a machine can do and more than Dr Wolf dreams of. But, dare I suggest that, perhaps, our learned friend has already experienced his glimpse of the future in one such parallel universe and managed to convey that image, via his right brain to its left half, for rationalization. In the same way, I am able to 'recall' knowledge of that network of time's energy circuits (or remember the future?) along which one can pass, toll free, to explore the uncharted universe.

French scientist Dr Jacques Vallée, whose studies of UFO phenomena are well known, has shown considerable interest in the 'multi-dimensional universe' concept, as he sees in it a logical explanation for the origin of UFOs which, he believes, travel from dimension to dimension, their ability to do so explaining many of their characteristics – may I add, along that aforementioned time-space network?

When parallel universes touch (or we inadvertently pass a little too close to the proximity of one of time's terminals) although we may perceive what we feel to be normality according to our present understanding of reality, the real test comes when we react to the situation in the same way that we would in our conscious world. Trying to turn on a light, for example, that refuses to respond to our manipulation of the switch, or shouting to attract the attention of someone nearby who appears oblivious of our presence and deaf to our cries. I can recall clearly one such experience when I was supposedly asleep. I found myself in a room in another period of what I assumed to be Earth time, the early part of the twentieth century, perhaps. A man was hastily ransacking the contents of a battered suitcase, as though searching desperately for something important. Someone entered the room stealthily behind him. I shouted to warn the searcher of an impending peril, but he did not or *could not* hear me. A hand holding a knife rose and fell with precision upon its victim, who clutched desperately at the curtains as he collapsed into the arms of death. To this day I could describe every detail of those curtains and the hands of the man. I recall moving backwards *through a wall* and promptly awoke. Psychics I knew at the time suggested I had been 'astrally projecting' which was why I could not be heard, and could vanish through the thick walls; but I could also have strayed into a parallel universe. Equally, someone from that very universe, or others that might reflect our conditions here on Earth, could be experiencing problems in communicating with us.

My late, and much loved, nanny used to have an old Victorian picture hanging over her bed that depicted a pretty little child venturing too near the edge of a decaying rustic bridge, beneath which a fast torrent rushed. Overshadowing her was a traditional Christian-type angel, and the caption read 'The Guardian'. One cannot help wondering whether many of the manifestations attributed to celestial beings and so-called 'guiding entities' are no more than brief glances into some parallel world, the inhabitants of which may well be either fragments of ourselves, or beings who have been watching us and trying to help us over life's many stiles, but unable to draw our attention to an appropriate signpost or wise course of action.

Another question I would like to put to those physicists with a metaphysical bent is: when I project my consciousness away from its physical vehicle, why does my body and everything around it become increasingly smaller and smaller until it is imperceptible? Wolf thinks that the answer to this and similar enigmas might lie in the world of subatomic particles, the strange behaviour of which prompted Hugh Everett III, a graduate student physicist at Princeton University, studying under the highly regarded physicist John Archibald Wheeler, to conceive of the parallel universe idea in 1957. In the subatomic world, the line between the material and the insubstantial is decidedly blurred, if not actually obscured. Experimentation continually poses the same question: when is a wave a wave, and when is it a particle? Although this inconsistent behaviour of particles, when confronted with two or more possibilities, now has a name – the *wave/particle duality* – the problem remains. The world of quantum research proceeded to spawn a host of semantics which continued to emphasize the problems on hand, *quantum wave function* or *probability wave*, for example, which is a mathematical formula that presents the possibilities of events occurring in wave patterns across space; *wave/packet*, to denote those subatomic entities that are neither fully particles nor fully waves.

In quantum mechanics, probability is a measure of possibilities that must somehow exist simultaneously, and because these possibilities affect or interact with each other, they effect changes in the physical properties of matter. The truth is that scientists are still very much in the dark when it comes to the behaviour of minute particles, and until further information is available the aforegoing and many other questions associated with this study must remain unanswered. (For the metaphysical implications see pp. 143–5).

Dark Matter

Science has recently bombarded us with a series of statements which infer that our own universe is 10 or even 100 times larger than it seems. The greater portion of the cosmos seem to have 'gone missing', we are told. According to Dr Michael Disney, Professor of Astronomy at University College, Cardiff, even conservative astronomers are now facing up to the remarkable discovery that even quite nearby regions of space must contain between ten and a hundred times more mass than they can presently account for. Around, within and between galaxies space appears to be dominated by massive invisible agencies which defy efforts at detection and mock the present theories of the universe. Disney's book, *The Hidden Universe*, was first published in 1984;

since then the evidence has rolled in. The publication of two books on the subject: *The Stuff of the Universe: Dark Matter, Mankind and the Coincidences of Cosmology*, by John Gribbin and Martin Rees, and *The Fifth Essence: the Search for Dark Matter in the Universe*, by Lawrence M. Krauss, received several pages of coverage in the weekend *Guardian* (23 June 1990). The *Guardian* science correspondent, Tim Radford, who has that rare gift – the ability to present scientific data in language comprehensible to the layman – treated his readers to some extraordinary data from these books, notably the cosmic string theory. He tells us that cosmic string – which according to physicists is theoretically possible and therefore presumed to exist – is 'very eerie, even supernatural stuff'. He describes this strange substance as:

> . . . almost infinitely thin: fine enough to whizz through the smallest atom without touching anything. It wriggles or oscillates across the universe at nearly the speed of light. It is either infinitely long, or in a loop a million light years across. It has only one disadvantage for anyone who gets threaded on it. It is heavy. One inch would weigh about ten million billion tons. That's why if a bit passed through your body you wouldn't feel it, you'd just feel the force of gravity bringing your extremities together at 10,000 mph (16,000 kpm).
>
> Cosmic string is a candidate for the dark side of creation. It may not exist but, just the same, scientists are looking out for it because it could answer the biggest question in the universe: where is most of it hidden?

The Super-string Theory

This theory, developed by Mike Green, of Queen Mary College, London, undoubtedly equates with the Gribbin/Rees premise. Dr Frank Close, writing on the subject in *The Particle Explosion*, seems to think that the theory predicts the existence of a whole shadow universe operating concurrently with our own. Close adds:

> the universe we know is formed from only one small part of these strings – a much heavier universe, existing in the same place as our own, would be made up of the heavier parts of the super-strings. There may be other universes or other dimensions on other parts of the strings.[3]

And so the search for dark matter, or the other 90 or 99 per cent of the universe, continues – with little success to date it would seem. This is because, as Radford suggests, all the candidates are 'dark horses'; the 'wimps' (weakly interacting massive particles) for example, and the 'machos' (massive compact halo objects) which have been suggested, but not found; neutrinos – notional particles that have neither charge nor mass which emerge from every cosmic nuclear reaction may be candidates, but only if they exhibit *some* mass, but there would appear to be too few of them to make their presence felt. Brown dwarfs, stars that never grew large enough to ignite, and magnetic monopoles – lonely things that have no polarity – have been discounted by Gribbin and Rees. So, back we come to the cosmic string or super-string – well, for the time being anyway.

Quarks and Other Subatomic Wonders

Before particle accelerators started to yield up their subatomic secrets, the standard model of particle physics held that all matter was composed of two kinds of particles, leptons and quarks, which interact and cluster together via the agency of four forces, strong, weak, electromagnetic, and gravitational. A lepton is described as any of a family of elementary particles including the electron, the muon and the tau particle, and their associated neutrinos, all having spin equal to 1/2 and masses less than those of the mesons. Quarks belongs to the family of subatomic particles believed to be among the fundamental constituents of matter. In much the same way that protons and neutrons make up atomic nuclei, these particles themselves are thought to consist of quarks. Quarks were named by Murray Gell-Mann, a California Institute of Technology physicist who was awarded the Nobel prize for his work with them. Gell-Mann took the name from a line from James Joyce's *Finnegan's Wake*, 'Three quarks for Muster Mark'. Quark is the German word for a cottage-cheese type of desert, and also German slang for 'nonsense'. Quarks, apparently, come in several varieties: Up, Down, Top (also called Truth), Bottom (also called Beauty), Strange and Charmed, and each of these in turn is subdivided into a colour: red, green and blue. A proton or neutron is made up of three quarks, one of each colour. Protons have two 'up' quarks and one 'down' quark, and neutrons two 'down' and one 'up'. Particles consisting of the other types of quarks can also be created, but their mass is greater and they quickly decay into protons and neutrons.[4] The following table illustrates the present standard model of leptons and quarks according to Lederman and Schramm.

Some theorists, notably Abdus Salam, a Pakistani physicist working in London, suggest that there is another level of particle

PARTICLES IN THE STANDARD MODEL

Generation	Leptons				Quarks			
	Particle name	Symbol	Mass at rest (MeV)	Electric charge	Particle name	Symbol	Mass at rest (MeV)	Electric charge
I	Electron neutrino	ν_e	About 0	0	Up	u	About 5	$+\frac{2}{3}$
	Electron	e^-	0.511	-1	Down	d	About 7	$-\frac{1}{3}$
II	Muon neutrino	ν_μ	About 0	0	Charm	c	1,500	$+\frac{2}{3}$
	Muon	μ^-	105.7	-1	Strange	s	About 150	$-\frac{1}{3}$
III	Tau neutrino	ν_τ	Less than 35	0	Top/truth	t	>41,000	$+\frac{2}{3}$
	Tau	τ^-	1,784	-1	Bottom/beauty	b	About 5,000	$-\frac{1}{3}$

reality below quarks. Salam calls these *preons* and argues that 'each quark consists of two preons, one defining flavour, the other defining colour.' (L. M. Lederman and D. N. Schramm, *From Quarks to the Cosmos*, p. 161). In support of their TOE theory (see p. 16) Lederman and Schramm propose that somewhere underneath it all there may well be just one force that provides all the particles and their interactions, which certainly makes sound metaphysical sense.

All this could be likened to a child lifting a large stone to discover a world of bizarre, fascinating and somewhat frightening creatures beneath it. One cannot help wondering whether the ancients had the right idea with their belief in an unending string of intermediaries existing in some invisible world between man and the Creator. The fact that they were seen in the context of gods, demons, nature spirits, angels, or whatever, scarcely matters. After all, the 'good daimons' of Gnosticism, the cherubim and seraphim of Chistianity, the satyrs and centaurs of Greek mythology or the animal-headed gods of Egypt and the Orient could surely hold their own against an 'up-quark', or a 'wimp'. Or perhaps that is just what many of them are? One is reminded of the conclusion drawn by lawyer and Cambridge classics scholar John Ivimy, who wrote: 'Classical historians traditionally dismiss tales of magic as unworthy of scholarly attention, but to us any mention of a witch's broomstick or a wizard's wand evokes the smell of a scientist's laboratory.'[6] So perhaps there was a time, long before the biblical Flood, when an advanced race of human beings existed who understood the secrets of super-strings and their intercosmic brethren rather better than we do today, and whose knowledge later degenerated into superstition and tribal folk lore?

Religious fundamentalists would doubtless regard all this as blasphemous, to say the least. But I prefer to heed the advice of Einstein: 'Religion without science is blind – science without religion is lame.' In other words, there is room for both, but one must be tempered with reason and the other with intuition. Perhaps the more enlightened among the gentlemen (and hopefully, before long, ladies) of the cloth are beginning to unite the scientifically unsubstantiated 'superstitions' of faith with the discoveries of science. Tony Grist, a former clergyman and now a poet and novelist, writing in the *Guardian* column 'Face to Faith' (21 January, 1990), commented:

> The visible, tangible cosmos is only one of a series of parallel universes that interpenetrate one another without contact or confusion, much as

radio waves of different frequencies can occupy the same space without losing their integrity. . .

The superstitions of 19th century materialism are now as *passé* as the superstitions of religion. And agnosticism tempered with open-mindedness is the only honest course. In our new enlarged cosmos anything might happen. Phenomena from flying saucers to the visions of St. Teresa of Avila could turn out to have their origins in some parallel universe which is as much a part of physical reality as we are.

Physicists have offered some rather bizarre examples of how the Uncertainty Principle is likely to manifest in the worlds of time and quantum, the best known of which are undoubtedly Schrö-dinger's Cat, Wigner's Friend, and the Einstein-Podolsky-Rosen paradox. In more recent times, these have been either disputed, or countered by such theories as Bell's theorem, Chew's bootstrap philosophy, and Bohm's hologram analogy. Since all of these may be seen as relevant to time, I shall include a few brief synopses. Fuller details may be obtained from works referenced in the Bibliography.

Schrödinger's Cat

The Austrain physicist, Erwin Schrödinger (1887–1961), who conceived of the wave theory of quantum mechanics, called attention to what has become known as the 'cat paradox'. The scenario Schrödinger set for his theory was that of a cat locked up in a box containing a Rube Goldberg device that will or will not emit cyanide gas depending on the outcome of a single quantum event – the radioactive discharge of an atom. The paradox lies in the fact that the cat could be in the box for a period of time wherein the probability is 50 per cent that the atom has discharged. If no one investigates to see what has happened, is the cat dead or alive? The Copenhagen school appeared to have no answer to this enigma, but students of the Parallel Universe theory would proclaim the cat both dead and alive in separate but equal worlds. The Zohar and Eysenck and Sargent definitions of this paradox are given in greater detail in Chapter 8 (p. 143), along with the metaphysical and psychological interpretations of some of the various manifestations of the phenomenon.

Wigner's Friend

The Wigner in question was quantum pioneer Professor Eugene Wigner, a colleague of Schrödinger whose 'friend' was a hypothetical person holding the cage containing the cat who might decide to look in to see what has happened. Will the cat be dead or alive? But let us imagine that professor Wigner's friend and the caged cat are together in a closed room. Wolf tells us:

> If the professor doesn't look in on the friend, even though the friend has looked at the cat, is the friend in a happy state of mind upon seeing a live cat, or a sad state of mind upon seeing a dead cat? According to quantum rules written in Copenhagen, until the professor looks, the friend's state cannot be decided. But according to the parallel universe thesis, the friend and the cat exist in two editions.[7]

The EPR Paradox

Named after physicists Albert Einstein, Boris Podolski and Nathan Rosen, what are generally known in physics as the EPR experiments deal with the problem of *locality* and *non-locality*. The locality in this context refers to situations where whatever occurs at a point in space and time depends only on the influences in the immediate vicinity of the event. Quantum mechanics is therefore considered as 'non-local'. Einstein, it seems, was highly sceptical of quantum mechanics, so he devised an experiment in which two particles interact and then separate to a considerable distance. Given these circumstances, the quantum state of the combined system has shown that a measurement performed on one particle affects the outcome of the measurements made on the other particle that has distanced itself considerably.

This appeared as something of an affront to Einstein's logic, so much so that he dubbed it 'spooky action-at-a-distance'.[8] This same experiment has been applied in parapsychological research and the conclusions reached suggest that an observer can affect an event that takes place at almost any distance away from him or her, indicating that the collapse of the wave function can be spatially invariant, while in certain treatments of this paradox the collapse can also display features of temporal invariance. In other words, what we have here are observation effects that are not limited by space or time constraints, and could therefore be seen to exhibit points in common with psi.[9]

Bell's Theorem

Three decades after Einstein and his co-workers had formulated their famous paradox, John Bell, a theoretical physicist at the European Centre for Particle Physics (CERN – Conseil Européen pour la Recherche Nucléaire), derived a theorem based on the EPR experiment, which showed the existence of local hidden variables to be inconsistent with the statistical predictions of quantum thinking, and therefore incompatible with Einstein's conception of reality. Experiments showed two photons to be so closely linked that space and time in no way influenced their instantaneous communication with each other in spite of Inner Time differences. In other words, they were communicating in Outer Time. This scenario is re-echoed in such esoteric practices as absent healing, and those popular link-ins and 'harmonic convergences' where people are instructed to visualize a clock with the hand set at, say, twelve noon before sending out their thoughts or prayers, which also employ the Outer Time communication mode.

The Bootstrap Philosophy

The originator and main advocate of this theory is physicist Geoffrey Chew. His bootstrap concept evolved from work undertaken with colleagues to construct a specific theory of particles. The bootstrap philosophy is seen as constituting the final rejection of the mechanistic world view in modern physics. It conceives of the universe as '. . . a dynamic web of interrelated events. None of the properties of any part of this web is fundamental; they all follow from the properties of the other parts, and the overall consistency of their mutual interrelations determines the structure of the entire web.'[10] Chew is one of a new order of physicists who adopt a more holistic view of science in that their theories border on the metaphysical. The same can also be said of David Bohm.

Bohm's Hologram Analogy

Professor David Bohm is seen by some physicists as having gone farther than anyone else in his field in studying the relationship between consciousness and matter in the scientific context. One of Bohm's main concerns was the notion of 'unbroken wholeness', and he viewed the non-local connections that are exemplified by the EPR experiment as contributory to his theory. Bohm turned to the hologram as an appropriate analogy, because each fragment of the shattered whole contains the image of the complete picture, albeit in less detail. Useful as it is in one context, however, Bohm was also aware of the limitations of his hologram analogy as a scientific model for the 'implicate order' at the subatomic level, so he coined his own term – holomovement – to describe his hypothesis. A full explanation of Bohm's conclusions is to be found in his book, *Wholeness and the Implicate Order*. Commenting on Bohm's idea, Capra writes: 'According to Bohm, space and time emerge as forms flowing out of the holomovement; they, too, are enfolded in its order.'[11] Lyall Watson later employed a similar hologram analogy to explain the metaphysical theory of reincarnation. (See Chapter 8, Endnote 7).

Black Holes

Wolf defines a black hole as:

> A spherical region of space which contains a gigantic gravitational field. The field is so large that everything on its surface is sucked into it, including light. Imagine a sphere that, like a magnet, attracts everything around it. Now let it suck in sunlight and you have a black hole.[12]

This region in space to which Wolf refers is caused by a star collapsing under its own gravitational force to such an extent that its gravitational field prevents any matter, light or other electromagnetic radiation leaving the region. In other words, it is a one-way ticket.

The term 'black hole' was coined in 1969 by the American scientist John Wheeler, and popularized in the John Taylor classic, *Black Holes*, in 1973. These phenomena subsequently have provided a fount of inspiration for science fiction writers and dramatists who have presented the public with strange tales of spaceships disappearing into one of them and ending up in some parallel universe or different period of time. Since we will be dealing with time warps as such in Chapter 4, let us leave that aspect of the black hole alone for the moment and concentrate on what black holes actually are from a scientific standpoint.

Black holes, it would seem, spell doom for some physicists. For example, John Gribbin tells us:

> Where enough matter is gathered together in one place – and 'enough' need only be the equivalent of a few Suns like our own – it seems, according to the equations of relativity theory, that gravity becomes the ultimate 'irresistible force', crushing the matter down into a literal point, a mathematical singularity, and crushing with it the very fabric of space-time. Before the singularity is reached, gravity around the superdense object is so strong that even light cannot escape, hence the term 'black hole'; the region within which escape is impossible and

ultimate collapse to this singularity is inevitable is bounded by the so-called 'event horizon'.[13]

All very scary to the layman, no doubt. But what occurs to me, as far as black holes are concerned, is that they might conceivably be the instruments of those quantum leaps that alter drastically the frequences or wavebands of certain types of matter, for example, convert the stuff of one universe to that of a parallel field, or even form a new universe in some other cosmic time zone and, as such, their connection with the energies of time are obvious. As a metaphysician, I tend to view the universe as a precise mechanism which is either self-programmed, or influenced by some incomprehensible Mind. Every component, therefore, has a clearly defined function to perform or role to play in the overall picture, and although we may fail to understand these specific capacities now, they will become increasingly obvious to us as our species evolves.

Gribbin makes one interesting statement that caught my eye, especially in the light of my own views regarding the 'circuitry of time':

> I have described the physical implications of the existence of holes in space, and the presence of space-time singularities in the Universe, in my book *White Holes*; the prospects which are, hypothetically at least, opened up by such holes for travel in space through a kind of cosmic subway have been elaborated by Adrian Berry in his own *The Iron Sun*. Here, of course, we want to know about the other aspect of this destruction of space-time by the intense gravity of a singularity, the prospects opened up for travel in time.[14]

Perhaps my inter-time network theory is not so far out after all. But then Gribbin's book was published in 1979, and scientific discoveries in this field have accelerated to such an extent over the past ten years that even the physicists are hard-pressed to keep up with them. In fact, of the many works I have encountered on the subject, most of which have been written by fully qualified scientists, several of the authors concerned appear to be totally unaware of the theories and findings of their contemporaries, while opinions differ considerably as to the interpretation of the research material available. Hawking's approach to black holes, for example, is essentially technical and concentrates more on their actual formation from collapsed stars. Those readers who are more interested in technical data are therefore recommended to Hawking's work, which is amply illustrated with appropriate diagrams. On the other hand, Davies, Gribbin and Wolf tend to adopt a wider approach, blending their interpretations of the cosmos with psychology, metaphysics and the humanities.

White Holes

While most of us have encountered the term 'black holes', either through the imaginative tales of science fiction or in the popular press, their polarity, 'white holes', are seldom mentioned. A white hole is defined as a hypothetical astrophysical object formed by the emergence of matter from a space-tme singularity through the event-horizon. Like black holes, white holes are associated with a space-time singularity, but whereas matter disappears into a black hole wherein it is forced out of the universe, it pours out of a white hole in what Gribbin describes as a kind of 'cosmic gusher'. Could we possibly be dealing with a system which absorbs matter, reorganizes it and then returns it to the universe? But is it *exactly the same matter* that is returned, or has some form of transmutation taken place during its journey into one 'hole' and out of the other? How do we know, for example, that new galaxies in the process of forming were not part of an ageing system that vacated its space in the universe for some transformative treatment in a black hole? The inference is that the birth and death of stars, or galaxies, come to that, is an ever-continuing process and could be likened to the cycle of birth, death and resurrection that is one of the essential tenets of esoteric belief. The ancient Egyptians subscribed to the idea of the *Khet Khet* or 'Double Fire', the fire of dispersion and the fire of solidification, personified by the goddesses Nephthys and Isis respectively. Nephthys was always the 'dark' or 'hidden' deity, while Isis carried the 'light' of solidification, as represented by her maternal aspect – she who gives birth to Horus, the new son (sun?). Basic cosmic knowledge concealed in a simple myth, the forces involved being personalized for explanatory convenience. But more of all this in Chapter 6.

Wormholes

Closely allied to black/white holes are wormholes, defined as openings in space that connect either to remote regions in one particular universe, or one universe with a parallel universe. The name 'wormhole' was coined by John Archibald Wheeler, and has since been employed by quantum topologists to describe points at which energy leaks from one universe to another. Wormholes arise inside black holes, and come in all shapes and sizes. For example, a tiny particle could be a wormhole if viewed from the microcosmic angle. Wolf quotes Hawking as pointing out, albeit elusively, that energy may not be the only thing that leaks between universes via wormholes: information and the concept of order are two other possibilities.[15] Some of the channels in time's labyrinthine circuitry are surely becoming more clearly defined.

'Hole' phenomena have sometimes been criticized as 'figments' of equations. If one is going to judge them against this criterion, however, it has to be said that it is those same equations that have produced the Big Bang theory. Theoretical physics has, of course, been the testing ground for many hypotheses, some of which, like the current space probes, have been ultimately proven while others still remain mysteries. And until those mysteries are solved empirically, to the satisfaction of all concerned, the 'in the black hole and out of the white one' will, no doubt remain as much an amusing premise as the *Khet Khet*.

Since the subject matter of our book is time, you may well ask what 'holes', be they black or white, have to do with the concept of time as an energy? The little information we do have from scientific sources would seem to reinforce the idea that the energies associated with these phenomena, whether they be related purely to the gravitational field or whether they may also carry other properties of which we are as yet unaware, would appear to have transformational qualities. From the purely metaphysical viewpoint, their association with time–energies would seem obvious since time is *the* great transformer. Somewhere along that 'channel of time/timelessness' that is speculated as existing between the black hole and its white polarity, a transmutation takes place, in much the same way that we each enter our 'black hole of death' along a dark tunnel into the white light beyond, and emerge into rebirth along a similar tunnel, to behold the light of the star we call our sun. Metaphysical eyewash? Hardly.

The work of Drs Lyall Watson, Helen Wambach, Edith Fiore, and many other erudite researchers of distinction within their own fields would seem to confirm the idea that what happens to us happens to everything else in all the different universes, including those we cannot as yet detect with our existing technology. This clearly defined cycle is repeated at all levels, with all things, from the minutest particle to the hub of the universe itself. We of the metaphysical fraternity like to refer to it as Cosmic Law. And the agent of its enactment? Time!

Endnotes

1. F. A. Wolf, *Parallel Universes*, p. 21.
2. *Ibid.* pp. 23–4.
3. *Flying Saucer Review*, Vol. 32, No. 3, 1987.
4. S. W. Hawking, *A Brief History of Time*, p. 65.
5. L. M. Lederman, and D. N. Schramm, *From Quarks to the Cosmos*, p. 111.
6. J. Ivimy, *The Sphinx and the Megaliths*, p. 96.
7. Wolf, *op. cit.* pp. 50–1.
8. P. Davies, *The Cosmic Blueprint*, p. 176.
9. H. J. Eysenck, and C. Sargent, *Explaining the Unexplained*, p. 144.
10. F. Capra. *The Tao of Physics*, p. 316.
11. *Ibid.* p. 353.
12. Wolf, *op. cit.* p. 321
13. J. Gribbin, *Time Warps*, p. 78.
14. *Ibid.* pp. 78–9.
15. Wolf, *op. cit.* p. 195.

4
Time Warps, Loops, Slips and Capsules

We live in the continual presence of our own experiences.
Time by itself does not exist.
LUCRETIUS (*c.* 95–*c.* 55 BC)

The world of time studies has developed a set of semantics all of its own, many of which mean little, if anything, to the layman. However, the entertainment profession has been quick to note the growing interest in the subject, and the media have accordingly bombarded their readers, listeners and viewers with a variety of articles and programmes on time, ranging from the highly technical to the fictionally ludicrous. Since many of us either have been, or still are, at a loss as to the difference between a time loop, a time slip, and a time warp, some elucidation is called for.

Time Warps

A time warp could be described in a single sentence as an imaginary distortion or interruption in the flow of time from past to future, featured typically in science fiction. Fans of the 'Dr Who' or 'Star Trek' series will be all too familiar with this scenario: the starship is progressing satisfactorily along its pre-selected route, the crew are about their business and serenity reigns. Then, suddenly, there are a series of bumps, bangs and other very obvious disturbances which usually involve everyone being dislodged from their seats, the instruments going haywire, lights flickering, and the navigator calling to the captain: 'Sir, we've been sucked into a time warp!'

What we, the viewers, are meant to gather from this is that there are strange pockets of energy dotted around the universe, and should some spaceship accidentally venture into one of these, it is liable to be catapulted into either the past or future in Earth time, or some parallel or uncharted universe. Escaping from this somewhat mind-baffling situation usually involves the craft returning to the exact point at which the entry into the time warp occurred, resetting the coordinates into reverse and, lo and behold, the ship is once again back on course. To fill out the storyline, however, numerous adventures, some pleasant and others less desirable naturally occur while the craft and its crew are encapsulated within the warp, but then, if we are honest, we all enjoy a good tale.

Scientists with a degree of imagination who are not afraid of risking their reputations have, from time to time, advanced mathematical formulae for the possible existence of time warps. In his book *Timewarps*, Dr John Gribbin tells us that the aspect of Einstein's theory of general relativity that is concerned with possible time travel in the future, which he sees as having some connection with a genuine time warp, is:

. . . the discovery that a gravitational field distorts both space and time in its vicinity, and in particular a clock in a strong gravitational field runs slow in much the same way as does a rapidly moving clock. If the gravitational field is strong enough, time effectively stands still, as it would for a clock travelling at the speed of light, and this is one way of understanding the phenomenon of black holes. . . At the boundary of a black hole, gravity is so intense that time stands still, and nothing ever emerges from a black hole because it would take an infinite time on clocks in the outside world for anything at the boundary – including light – to break free.

Inside a black hole, time as we know it (together with space as we know it) ceases to exist. . .[1]

So, are we therefore being told that time warps are synonymous with black holes, or could we also deduce from the aforesaid that black holes are multifunctional energy cells useful to the universe in more ways than one? Using the computer analogy I have suggested in earlier chapters, black holes or time warps could be equated with those commands that move whole sections of input from one position to another, rearrange them, and illustrate various angles or probabilities on the visual display unit.

As we have discussed in the previous chapter, the curved space-time postulated by Einstein, with its accompanying singularities, suggest there are regions where gigantic distortions occur, and where the normal laws of physics no longer apply. These distortions are seen by some scientists, notably Wolf, to contain gateways to other universes, a view which he supports with the

Einstein-Rosen bridge, which he sees as the Einsteinian contribution to his own parallel universe theory.[2]

The specific property of black holes and of time warps, if we are to associate one with the other, is gravity, the key force that holds the universe together (see also Chapter 2). Therefore, an appreciation of gravity is essential to an understanding of the cosmos. But since the gravity involved in the black-hole phenomenon would also appear to be linked with the timelessness aspect of time's energies, I propose that the forces of gravity and time are closely and inexplicably linked. However, that could also be said of all those other energy sources that scientists have striven to unite under the single canopy of the Grand Unified Theory. So why not consider time to be the ultimate link in the subtle chain of cosmic coincidences that continue to baffle science?

Coming back to my 'railway track' analogy, the black hole might be seen to equate with a scheduled stopping point, and the time warp with (a) a signal malfunction that has altered the points and caused the vehicle to deviate from its original journey, or (b) a slight derailment that can be corrected if the engine is shunted back to the point of failure and the signal coordinates corrected.

I cannot help feeling that Dr Gribbin is correct in his assumption that both time warps and black holes do form part of the intricate network that will eventually prove to be the 'open sesame' to time travel, and one wonders whether he, or any of his fellow physicists, have also arrived at the conclusion that time is an energy in itself? If we are to accord any credence to the law of synchronicity, much loved by Carl Jung, I doubt very much if I am alone in my beliefs concerning time and its possible use as a future source of *universal* energy.

Time Loops

Wolf defines these as 'journeys that loop from present to future and then backward to the present, or journeys that start in the present and go back in time and then return to the present, or any combination thereof.' Such loops, he tells us, 'are not forbidden by the laws of physics, particularly if the starting and ending points are at the same time and space but in separate parallel universes.'[3]

The fact that the subject of time is an eminently saleable commodity may be evidenced in the popularity of films such as 'Back to the Future' and the TV series 'Quantum Leap'. The makers of these have hastened to cash in on the possibility of our being able to move backwards and forwards in linear Earth time, although after viewing a few episodes of the latter I failed to see what bearing it had on the real meaning of a quantum leap, since these phenomena would not, by definition, appear to be limited in their manifestation to time-hopping for the purpose of correcting past mistakes. However, since anything appears to be possible in the present climate of *avant garde* scientific and popular sci-fi thinking, I could be wrong.

Various fictional stories have been written about people who have returned to a certain point in the linear past to discover that what they fervently believed in had never actually taken place. So, in order to put the history books to rights, and accommodate the beliefs held by many, they assumed the role or roles of the personality concerned and played out the drama as the people of today believe it to have been. One such book was Michael Moorcock's *Behold the Man*, and another was Ward Moore's *Bring the Jubilee*. All good sci-fi stuff, but could it really happen? Could one person really change our whole evolutionary pattern by returning to a former era and introducing an action that was latterly to influence world culture. Well, I suppose it depends on how and from where in the cosmic scheme of things the picture is to be viewed.

The metaphysician would assure you, however, that there is a timeless, infinite point in time at which all time is one, and at which every conceivable permutation of life and experience, at every level throughout every universe, converges and is instantaneously present. No doubt some readers may subscribe to the belief that this process involves the presence of a single Intelligence who has, perhaps, had a hand at stage-managing the whole cosmic scenario. That being the case, as we all know, any good manager is adept at delegating so, as Shakespeare wisely observed: 'There are more things in heaven and earth, Horatio, than are dreamt of in your philosophy.'

If such phenomena as time loops do exist, they are probably no more than return tickets along the circuits of time, and there will eventually come an era when these can be obtained for whatever purpose is designated. Metaphorically speaking, however, I would strongly advise future time travellers to give a thought to the possibility of signal failure, derailment, or even some other intelligence of less than benign intent playing tricks with the signal box – remember Schrödinger's cat. What I am trying to say is, even if we do eventually come to understand the use of time as an energy there are always those unsuspected contingencies to cope with, and that uncertainty principle will be found to function just as unpredictably in Outer Time as it does in Inner Time.

Time Slips

It is at this point that science and human experience either come together, or lock antlers, as the case may be. The concept of the time slip involves the consideration that there are certain locations in the universe, and on our own planet for that matter, where the connection between Outer and Inner Time is tenuous. Occultists used to (and some still do) refer to these as points between the physical and subtle worlds (real and imagined worlds in the eyes of scientific orthodoxy) at which the veil is thin, and therefore more easily penetrated from either side. Over the years these have become associated with what are termed 'power centres', 'ley lines', and allied phenomena, much of which is still viewed as total rubbish by many scientists.

The strange thing about time slips is that they are often encountered by the totally unsuspecting, as in the case of the two English ladies whose story is well documented in the book *An Adventure*, which first appeared in 1911 although the actual event took place in 1901. The two ladies concerned, Miss Anne Moberly, a former Principal of St Hugh's College at Oxford, and Miss Eleanor F. Jourdain, who had been vice-principal for some years and who succeeded Miss Moberly as head of the college, were not the sort of ladies normally given to flights of fancy. What happened was this: on a holiday in France, they suddenly found themselves walking together in the Trianon of the Palace of Versailles in the year 1789, and coming upon figure after figure from that unfamiliar past.

For some years the story was published with fictitious names, as the ladies in question both held important educational posts and were obviously anxious to preserve their integrity. However, their true identity leaked out and later editions of the book were adjusted accordingly. The feeling they both described, of over-whelming depression and heaviness, has latterly proved of interest to both psychologists and physicists. Miss Moberly commented: 'Everything suddenly looked unnatural, therefore unpleasant; even the trees behind the buildings seemed to have become flat and lifeless *like a wood worked on tapestry*. There were no effects of light and shade, no wind stirred in the trees. It was all intensely still.'[4] The events described, clothing, layout of the gardens and other physically observable phenomena were later checked and found to be historically accurate to the finest detail.

I have experienced time slips myself, and can vouch for the feeling of flatness and depression that accompanies their manifestation. I have also experienced multidimensional awareness (the simultaneous mental computation of more than one state of reality or time-zone), which probably relates to some area of the brain that will eventually be triggered into general use once time has been conquered, otherwise exposure to a phenomenon of this kind could prove mind-blowing for many.

Certain places have become famous for what are believed to be time slips – the Bermuda Triangle, for example, although the theory that ships and aircraft that disappeared in the area were transported into some other dimension or parallel universe has now been shattered by the discovery of several of the missing planes, almost intact, on the ocean floor. A book entitled *The Philadelphia Experiment*, which was later made into a film, was based on the idea that a large ship could be made invisible so that it could safely penetrate enemy waters. But what happened was that the technology misfired, projecting the ship and its entire crew into some alternative world, one member eventually ending up in the future. Fortunately for him, the science of the future period in which he found himself had conquered time, and one of their time travellers was able to return him to the year and place where he belonged.

Science fiction? Who knows? After all, what does happen to those countless people who leave their homes one day and are never seen again? The possibility of many of them having been murdered, or simply disappearing deliberately to escape from some family situation they were unable to handle must obviously be taken into account. There are, however, some instances that defy explanation, which certain writers have specialized in collecting and presenting in book form, doubtless with more than a little embroidery. So, although the majority of disappearances probably have a very rational explanation, there is always the odd one here and there that hints of a time slip into which an unsuspecting victim has accidentally fallen.

The Misses Moberly and Jourdain were fortunate in that they simply witnessed their scene and did not become a part of it. I knew an elderly man of great erudition and commonsense who underwent a similar experience which he related to me first hand. A member of one of the aristocratic families, he resided on a large estate in Scotland which housed an ancient castle. Being a countryman, he often took walks across the fields, and one day, when he was feeling particularly fit, he decided to broaden his horizons and enjoy some different views. After covering several fields he suddenly came upon an old Scottish steading, complete with cottage, outbuildings, stream and livestock. 'Strange,' he thought, 'I've never seen that farm before, how stupid of me!' He noticed some figures outside the cottage who appeared to be dressed in the style of another period. He hailed them, but they appeared not to hear him; only the animals turned their heads and gazed curiously. He made his way back to the castle and enquired about his new discovery. He was informed that there was no steading in that area of the estate. 'But I saw it in great detail,' he insisted. 'In fact, I'll take you there and show you.'

When they arrived at the location in question there was no steading to be seen, only open fields, undulating land and a small stream. Puzzled and somewhat mortified, he returned home. Being a man of education and above average intelligence, however, he declined to leave the matter there. During the ensuing days he made numerous enquiries and checked old records in Edinburgh. Sure enough, there had been a steading on that spot in the eighteenth century but it had been demolished many years earlier, however, the description of the property was exact. As he told me his story the thing that intrigued me was that the humans he saw were unable to see or hear him, whereas the animals appeared fully aware of his presence.

One is tempted to wonder how much of Outer Time animals do perceive. I know that my cats certainly see and sense things that are not recorded by the five human senses. I also believe that they are aware beforehand of when they are going to die.

From the evidence available it would seem that there are points in the aura of the Earth through which contact with other time-zones, alternative frequencies or parallel universes can be effected with ease. Although I may write of a technology that will eventually enable us to negotiate the time network and harness its energies, I am also of the opinion that the human mind has the propensity for achieving this without the technological nuts and bolts.

Time Capsules

A time capsule has been defined as a sealed container preserving articles and records of contemporary culture for study in the distant future. In this context, however, time capsules would only be seen as dealing with information concerning the history of mankind which is generally accepted by historians and anthropologists. But what if there are time capsules that contain information of a more distant kind, such as that relating to the archaic, prehistoric past of which, if we are honest, we have little knowledge, and other worlds that may occupy time-zones not directly concomitant or in contact with our own?

Various hypotheses have been advanced by both scientists and metaphysicians regarding the use of material objects as 'tapes' or 'discs' for information from the past, or even the future for that matter, ancient stones being high up on the list. The fact that the megaliths of past cultures appear to have been erected on sites that are suspected of harbouring geophysical faults – those places in the Earth's substructure where there are different types of rock – has inspired many people to believe that it is the stones themselves that are the time capsules.

In the early 1980s Dr Don Robins, an inorganic chemist researching at the Institute of Archaeology, discovered among other things that stone circles, such as the Rollrights, in Oxfordshire, appeared to enclose natural force fields and that at the time of the equinoxes, in March and October, the stones emitted regular ultrasonic signals, regardless of whether or not the sun was visible and quite independently of weather conditions. As the year draws on towards the solstices, the signals fade away. Another interesting phenomenon observed by Dr Robins and his crew was that the level of natural radioactivity was always higher outside the circle than inside, often by a factor of two. They were also found to exclude cosmic radiation, indicating some kind of shielding afforded either by the circular formation of the stones themselves, or the natural energy emitted by the Earth within the circle. The indications are therefore of a significant relationship between geological fault lines, the sites of these circles, and electromagnetic radiation.

Much of the phenomena formerly associated with UFOs and allied manifestations has been traced back to geophysical diturbances that affect the electromagnetic field to the extent that people living within the radius, or passing through it, are often afflicted by hallucinations or psychokinesis (PK). Over a period of many years researchers have collected volumes of information from people who claim to have witnessed strange luminescent phenomena in the regions of standing stones or other megalithic structures, some of whom declared that the phenomenon actually effected a kind of telepathic response, dimming its brightness or even ceasing its activities upon a mental request. But if we are to pay any heed to the Gaia hypothesis this is not surprising since it conceives of the Earth as a living organism in its own right, to which some of its followers have also ascribed a degree of intelligence equal to, or even in advance of, that which we possess at this point in our evolution.

UFO buffs are not the only people to witness phenomena of the kind that could be seen as arising from disturbances in the Earth's electromagnetic field. During the Second World War pilots found themselves being 'buzzed' by similar supraphysical manifestations that also appeared to respond to thought power. So, maybe it is not the stones themselves that are the time capsules, but the very ground upon which they were erected. The peoples of ancient times were much less left-brain hemisphere orientated than we are today and tended to use their minds more instinctively or intuitively than modern man. They were, perhaps, more aware of those sensitive spots on the body of Gaia and duly acknowledged them by building stone temples, either as places of worship or simply as markers of 'sacred sites'.

Ley lines, those subtle veins of energy that are believed to criss-cross our planet, called 'dragon lines' by the Chinese, or 'fairy lines' by the Celts, appear to link these sites to each other. Interestingly, ley lines have been found to run along fault lines which frequently intersect at stone circles. If so, it follows that the electromagnetic energy and its resulting atmospheric phenomena are likely to be stronger at those places than in the surrounding countryside. If there are such things as natural time capsules, I would suggest that they form part of the brain of Gaia, wherein must be stored the record of everything that has occurred on her surface since she was 'born'. Working on that assumption, anyone sufficiently sensitive to tap into her memory banks could add considerably to what science already knows. The sad truth, however, lies in the fact that many of those trained in the scientific disciplines tend to become so left-brain orientated that they dismiss right-brain promptings out of hand, and this applies particularly to those who hold positions of authority within the scientific establishment. Fortunately, some scientists are slowly coming round to this realization, and the recently formed Venture Research Unit, founded by Dr Don Braben, aims to obtain research grants that will promote the growth of 'creative science', and cover both the fundamental and applied aspects of genuine scientific inquiry. (For those interested, at the time of writing, the address of the Venture Research Unit is: BT Britannia House, Moore Lane, London EC2.)

The Stone Computers

While every standing stone may not be a time capsule in itself, there is now little doubt that at least some of the people responsible for their erection were familiar with time's rhythms. Gribbin states categorically that 'there is no longer any doubt that Stonehenge *is* an astronomical computer, and very little room to doubt that this is the purpose for which it was built.'[5] Gribbin fortifies his case with the discoveries of Professors Fred Hoyle, Colin Renfrew and Gerald Hawkins among others. He is at variance with those who see the originators of these megaliths as having received their knowledge and impetus from eastern Mediterranean, Greek or Egyptian sources. A combination of radio-carbon techniques and tree-ring dating (dendrochronology) has helped archaeologists to date ancient sites more accurately, with the result that historians and members of other disciplines associated with the study of the archaic are being obliged to do some rethinking.

According to Gribbin, the megalithic tombs predated the pyramids by hundreds of years. Although I am prepared to accept that an advanced culture did exist in and prior to what we refer to as the Mesolithic, or Middle Stone Age (estimated to have begun around 9000 BC), I do not see the necessity to separate it from similar cultures arising in Egypt, the Mediterranean area and elsewhere along the Atlantic seaboard in the same period. An alternative view is offered by John Ivimy in his book *The Sphinx and the Megaliths*. Both scholars engage in considerable detail on the subject and both opinions are worthy of consideration, since they each present a different piece of the jigsaw.

The Pyramids

Metaphysicians are inclined to believe that the ancients probably knew more about the mathematical and geometrical symbols of time than we do today, the pyramids being but one example of this. Why articles placed under scale models of the Great Pyramid should defy the normal wear and tear of time has puzzled many scientists. The pyramid shape has also been observed to produce strange effects on the human mind. Some years ago, while attending a popular New Age festival, I was shown to a scale model of the Great Pyramid large enough to accommodate a person, and invited to sit inside and see what I 'felt'. Being a little suspicious of that kind of thing, and also somewhat reticent to play guinea-pig, I turned to Swami Rama, an Eastern mystic who happened to be standing nearby, and suggested that he had 'first go'. Being a more mature and secure person than myself at that time, the Swami immediately agreed and in he went. Encouraged by his calm attitude I gained the confidence to follow after him. What I experienced was a temporary cessation of time, as though both the past and future were momentarily displayed before me. I have had several experiences of multidimensional awareness since then, and now realize that these have been taking place for me since babyhood, but I simply had not recognized them for what they were.

Upon emerging from the pyramid the Swami asked me what I had felt and seen. I told him, and he assured me that he had experienced exactly the same phenomena and had, in fact, repeated it to those nearby while I was still inside the structure. I have since learned a lot more concerning geometrical design and time, but since much of this is purely subjective, it needs to be tested and confirmed scientifically before more can be said on the subject. Researchers with a mathematical bent will find lots of interesting data in Peter Lemesurier's book *The Great Pyramid Decoded*, which confirms my own belief that as far as knowledge of the universe is concerned, we are by no means the first on the scene.

A scientific project, organized by the United Arab Republic in 1967–9, to probe the Chephren pyramid in search of some hitherto undiscovered burial material yielded up some strange results. Normal X-rays not being considered powerful enough to penetrate the stonework, Dr Luis Alvarez, a Nobel prizewinner for physics and director of the Lawrence Radiation Laboratory at the University of California, suggested his cosmic ray detection equipment might fit the bill, since this technology had been developed to measure the radiation particles bombarding the Earth from outer space. It was therefore assumed that if the equipment were placed in the existing burial chamber in Chephren's pyramid the amount of radiation reaching the chamber through the stone network could be recorded on magnetic tape and any deviation in the solidity of the structure noted, making it comparatively easy to trace any burial chambers that had not, as yet, been discovered.

The complicated radiation detectors were duly installed and a considerable amount of cosmic-ray information was collected, and there was certainly enough data to answer the original query. Lauren Yazolino, of California University, ran two tapes through the computer and was satisfied that the equipment was functioning correctly. Dr Alvarez visited the pyramid and collected the recorded tapes from his apparatus and then promptly left without making any comment on his findings. Dr Amir Gohed, of Egypt's El Shams University, Cairo, who was left in charge of the equipment once the American had left, explained that a complete deadlock has been reached. His only significant comment was:

> It defies all the known laws of science and electronics. The taped results are scientifically impossible! The recordings from which we hoped a great discovery would be made are a jumbled mass of meaningless symbols. The two tapes which should be exactly similar are totally different. Either the geometry of the pyramid is substantially erroneous, which we know it is not, or there is a mystery which is beyond explanation. Call it what you will – occultism, the curse of the pharaohs, sorcery or magic, there is some force at work in Chephren's pyramid that defies all the known laws of science.[6]

The experiment was never repeated again. To my knowledge, there have been no further comments on this phenomenon, and no doubt someone in some parallel universe is chuckling up his or her sleeve, as we glibly dismiss as impossible that which does not appear to conform to our *known* scientific laws. Of course, it has nothing to do with Pharaonic PK or any such nonsense; we have simply not yet come to terms scientifically with the true nature of time's energies.

Crop Circles – Time Indicators?

The escalating number of appearances and the increasing complexity of crop circles are another phenomenon that some believe may be associated with time. There would certainly seem to be some connection between the points at which they manifest and electromagnetic static emitted in the areas concerned, as they occur more frequently in the heavily faulted western half of the United Kingdom. Many explanations have been advanced as to what they are or what they represent, including student pranks; freak winds; an SOS from Gaia to her 'relatives' in outer space asking for assistance; messages from these intelligences acknowledging her plea and promising help; glyphs from an archaic form of writing; warnings to humankind of an impending cosmic disaster; maps of forthcoming planetary movement within our solar system; or the arrival/discovery of some hitherto concealed heavenly body, and so forth. (This is covered in greater detail in Ralph Noyes' book *The Crop Circle Engima,* Gateway Books.)

Perhaps if the various designs and locations were categorized and submitted to computer analysis some cohesive pattern might emerge that would help us to understand   (a) what we are dealing with and   (b) how to react, assuming we are able to make any sense of the results. The odd hoax there may well be, but it would be wiser to reserve judgement until more evidence of one kind or another is forthcoming.

A recent investigation was made of the crops that had been swirled into the formations. Richard Beaumont, writing in *Kindred Spirit* Vol. 1, No. 12, (Autumn 1990) reports:

In Stroud the HSC (UK and Ireland) Limited Laboratory provides a specialised service where crystalline structures from blood are analysed and crystalline patterns of herbs can be matched to those of the patient. This is all part of the Spagyrik process which is unique to each individual's needs and which has been successful in treating patients holistically.

This process being one of 'energy medicine' was applied to the cereal crop from various circles with very interesting results.

From the photographs it is clear that there is a noticeable change in the energy patterns of the corn from inside the circle to that of the control sample which was taken from the outside of the field. This is just an interim finding as experiments are still being carried out, and a report will be published later this year.

Genetic Time Capsules?

The eminent Soviet scientist, Professor Ivan A. Efremov, chose to express his *avant garde* ideas on time in the form of a novel. In *The Razor's Edge*, Efremov raises the possibility that our cells contain time recordings of innumerable ancestors, the human organism carrying the accumulated experiences of numerous generations, from the caveman to the astronaut. This he sees as a more logical answer to the idea of reincarnation, which his scientific training renders him unable to accept.[7] I have encountered this argument on many previous occasions, and observation and research have obliged me to arrive at the following conclusions: our genes definitely carry the history of our formery ancestry, but there is another factor to consider – the psyche which, if sufficiently powerful, can overprogramme genetic influences. However, this comprises part of the subject matter for Chapter 8.

Antimatter

Descending once more into the 'accepted' realities of rational

The extraordinarily complex crop circle formation which appeared at
Alton Barnes.

science, there is one discovery made in the physical world that is
connected with the energy of time: this is the concept of antimatter,
or 'antiparticle', as Hawking prefers to call it. In the early 1930s
the British mathematical physicist Paul Adrien Maurice Dirac,
who had been working on a combination of quantum theory and
special relativity, made discoveries that indicated the existence of
another kind of matter that had never previously been observed –
antimatter – deducing his famous Dirac Equation purely by
mathematical intuition.

Fortunately, the equation was taken seriously and later experiments, notably the work of American physicist Carl Anderson,
proved the existence of the positron, or anti-electron, the first step
in the discovery and identification of antimatter. Since then
antimatter has been consistently produced in the laboratory.
Antimatter does not survive for long, however. Positive energy
particles will seek out any gaps in the negative energy sea, and if
an ordinary electron encounters such a hole it will vanish into it,
emitting an acknowledging gamma ray as it takes its leave of our
universe. Davies comments: 'This process is the reverse of pair
creation, and is seen as the encounter of an electron with a
positron, followed by their mutual annihilation. Thus, whenever
antimatter meets matter, explosive disappearances result.'[8] Hawking confirms this in simple terms in his glossary: 'Each type of
matter particle has a corresponding antiparticle. When a particle
collides with its antiparticle, they annihilate, leaving only energy.'[9]

Although these colliding particles of matter and antimatter

appear to cancel each other out, as far as this universe is concerned, perhaps the very act of their collision serves to catapult them into some other cosmic time zone wherein they are reborn at another frequency, their farewell gamma ray being no more than the flame of their afterburners following rapid take-off into the circuits of time? Just a thought. There is also an in-depth metaphysical interpretation of the antimatter phenomenon which I shall be dealing with in Chapter 8.

Regarding antimatter, some scientists, Paul Davies, for example, have posed the intriguing question: why does the universe consist of almost 100 per cent matter, antimatter being conspicuous by its absence? The textbook answer would seem to be that at some stage during the Big Bang, the matter/antimatter symmetry was broken and we ended up with a surfeit of one and a dearth of the other. There is a metaphysical belief, also favoured by a few open-minded scientists, that nothing in the universe really ceases to exist, but simply changes form. Could we, therefore, speculate that there may well be a universe parallel with our own which was composed of the antimatter ejected when the first excess of matter over antimatter took place? This is believed to have happened seconds after the initial explosion. The quarks involved in this process are estimated to have taken only one microsecond to coalesce into nuclear particles, so by the end of the first second the remaining antimatter would have been negated by contact with matter.[10]

Not all scientists, however, concur with the concept of the reversal of time's arrow and its implications, as far as the theorized worlds of antimatter and parallel universes are concerned. Drs Coveney and Highfield have stated their reasons cogently, and with authority in their book *The Arrow of Time*. They view Newtonian determinism with a degree of scepticism, and use the fact of evolution and the existence of biological rhythms to reinforce their arguments. While acknowledging the intricate relationship that exists between matter, antimatter, spatial symmetry and the two directions of time, they assure their readers that the famous CPT theorem, developed by G. Lüders (1954) and Wolfgang Pauli (1955) can also be used to explain how time symmetry can be broken to give an arrow of time. The CPT theorem was so named because symmetry is tested by the combination of:

  * C Charge conjugation, by means of which matter is converted into antimatter;

★ P   Parity inversion, which converts spatial coordinates into their mirror images;

★ T   Time reversal, which reverses the direction of time.[11]

Coveney and Highfield certainly make a good case for time's arrow, and in many ways they are correct in that there does appear to be a forward directional impulse in linear time, as we experience it on Earth. But the laws of physics would also seem to caution us to keep an open mind regarding dimensions about which we are still almost completely in the dark. We should also refrain from prejudging conditions in those universes that, once discovered and charted, may well prove to function within an entirely different set of physical laws from those that operate within the frequencies of our own physical universe. The learned doctors have, however, made some interesting observations regarding the effect of the passage of time on the evolution of *Homo sapiens* and the other life forms with which we share the bosom of Gaia. I shall be dealing with these in some detail in subsequent chapters.

To return to the pro–determinism and parallel universe lobby, it has been postulated that a parallel universe running backward in time, from our viewpoint, may well be composed of antimatter. Therefore, were we to take a physical trip into one, via the agency of a black hole, we could well meet our antiself and – whoosh, we would both cease to exist. Or would we? In speculating whether two time travellers, a man and a woman, from anti-universes could ever communicate with each other, Wolf suggests that the answer might depend on whether or not they are really living in reversed time streams. If this was the case their future would be our past. The light in their universe would travel forward in time and therefore not be seen by the travellers crossing the twilight zone. He tells us:

> All of their light will pass into the past singularity. It's going the wrong direction in time, so to speak, to be seen by him.
>
> Thus she will not see him and he will not see her. If, by the way, she does come from a universe running backward in time compared with ours, she would also be made of antimatter, but that's another matter to worry about.
>
> But even though her past may be our future as far as we can tell, we could be wrong. What's going backwards for us may indeed also be backward for them. Their universe, in other words, may actually proceeed normally from what we calculate is the past to the future.[12]

So, we cannot really be sure. All we do know about antimatter is what we have observed in the behaviour of particles, and assuming the notion that the macrocosm and microcosm simply reflect each other at different frequencies, it would seem logical to deduce that solar systems, stars, galaxies, and indeed the whole universe, might follow the same pattern. If there is one element that is common to each and every one of these processes, at all levels within the universe, it is *time*. Without the passage of time, be it a microsecond or less or a million linear years, there would be no matter or antimatter, none of the nuclear reactions that create galaxies and universes, no evolution taking place in this or that section of any universe, be it acknowledged as real or not – and certainly no *us*.

Endnotes

1. J. Gribbin, *Timewarps,* p. 74.
2. F. A. Wolf, *Parallel Universes,* p. 143.
3. *Ibid.* p. 329.
4. A. Moberly, and E. F. Jourdain *An Adventure*, pp. 45–6.
5. Gribbin, *op. cit.* pp. 5–6.
6. P. Donaghy, *Prediction*, March 1986.
7. A. Tomas, *Beyond the Time Barrier*, pp. 64–6.
8. P. Davies, *Other Worlds*, p. 86.
9. S. Hawking, *A Brief History of Time*, p. 183.
10. P. Davies, *The Cosmic Blueprint*, p. 127.
11. P. Coveney, and R. Highfield, *The Arrow of Time*, p. 139.
12. Wolf, *op. cit.* pp. 163–4.

5
Time's Periodic Cycles

The arrow of time is a tool for expanding our knowledge, not a device for concealing ignorance.
COVENEY AND HIGHFIELD[1]

Over the centuries, certain cycles of periodicity have been calculated as exerting a degree of influence over the life cycles of the denizens of the planet Earth. These have ranged from the observations of the scholars and philosophers of the great civilizations of the past to the prognostications of modern scientists concerning weather patterns and other global phenomena. No doubt some of the following will have a more familiar ring about them than others, but each bears some relevance to the study of time as a whole.

The Saros Cycle

Astronomers have long recognized that the sequence of solar and lunar eclipses recurs every 18 years 11⅓ days, or 223 lunations. In other words, the centres of the sun and moon return to almost the same relative places, so the eclipses of the next period recur in approximately the same order. But because the length of the cycle includes one-third of a day, the zone of visibility is shifted 120 degrees, or one-third of a cycle, to the west each time. The Chaldeans, who were adept at astronomy and astrology, named this the Saros cycle (Greek, from Babylonian *sāru* 3600 years. The modern use is apparently based on a misinterpretation of the original cycle as one of 18.5 years) and magical powers were attributed to it that would one day be instrumental in causing the destruction of the world.

Although some scientists may dismiss this premise as superstitious nonsense, that does not mean that Saros has no bearing on earthly affairs. In fact, the French psychologist and statistician Michel Gauquelin cites his fellow countryman Le Danois as emphasizing the great importance that the Saros cycle can have on our lives. Le Danois claimed that the combined gravitational pull of the sun and moon acts on the tides, causing widespread disturbances in bodies of water that may account for the changes in climate over the centuries. Although many climatologists were inclined to think that Le Danois was guilty of stretching the facts to suit his fancy, the observations of another hydraulic engineer, E. Paris-Teynac, showed a similar pattern for large rivers, the Nile in particular.

Dates available on Nile tides go back 4000 years, and from these records some strange facts emerge. Rhythmic variations that coincide with astronomical cycles are clearly in evidence. Paris-Teynac identified an eleven-year variation that accords with the sunspot cycle, and eighteen-year periods corresponding to the Saros cycle that reflect the sun-moon eclipse intervals. These periods suggested to him that Saros really does increase the water level in some parts of the world. In other words, when sun-moon eclipses occur at certain points, the likelihood of some celestial drama is increased.

Ice Age Cycles

Attempts have also been made to relate the gravitational influence of the planets to the Ice Ages. In 1938, the Serbian astronomer M. Milankovitch tried to use them to explain the succession of glacial epochs. The climatic curves he calculated apparently corresponded rather accurately to the curves of the glacial advances. In 1956, Hans Suess, of the University of California, noted that the same curves also follow the cycles of temperature changes in the oceans over the same geological period.

Although Milankovitch's figures were met with considerable scepticism by many in the scientific community, George Gamov, of the University of Colorado, rallied to his defence with the statement:

> Despite the objections of some climatologists who claim that a few degrees difference in temperature could not have caused the glacial periods, it seems that the old Serbian was right. Therefore we have to conclude that, although the planets are without influence on the lives of the individuals (as the astrologers would have it), they certainly affect the life of men, animals, and plants through the long geological periods.[2]

It is now generally acknowledged that the sun and moon can affect health. In 1940, Dr William Peterson noted that deaths caused by tuberculosis were most frequent seven days before the full moon, and sometimes eleven days afterwards. He was able to relate this pattern to the pH content of the blood, the ratio of acidity to alkalinity of which varies according to the lunar cycle of terrestrial magnetism. Since then, the evidence of correspondences between lunar phases and various biological phenomena have poured in, while there has also been a deal of information confirming the effect of sunspots on both people and weather.

Soviet scientists have tended to be less sceptical of the effects of extraterrestrial bodies on both the Earth itself and human affairs in general. For example, the Soviet astronomer, R. P. Romachuk, saw the 'aspects' to which astrologers pay so much attention responding to scientific laws. 'It is the positions of the Sun, Jupiter and Saturn that determine sunspot activity', he tells us, his conclusions being based on a series of charts and observations over a period of time. Andrew Tomas cites the comments of A. Gangnus in the Russian magazine *Znanie-Sila*:

> In ancient times astrologers attempted to predict the future by the respective positions of the planets. Who knows, this may not be so absurd. If the respective positions of the planets really influence the sun, then astronomical tables could become data for helio-geophysical and even long-range climatic forecasts.

The Soviet astronaut A. A. Leonoff, and Dr V. I. Lebedeff, also stated: 'The number of car accidents increases four times on the second day after the solar flare-ups, as compared with the days when the sun is calm.'[3] Suicides, it seems, also increase four or five times above the normal rate during periods of high solar disturbance.

Time and the Greenhouse Effect

The 'greenhouse' scare has produced volumes of scientific speculations regarding the effects of different cycles on our planet as a whole, and our weather in particular. Professor Hugh Lamb, of the University of East Anglia's climatic research unit, considered to be one of the world's leading climatologists, in an interview with the *Evening Standard* (27 February 1990) stated that Britain may be lashed by gales of up to 179 mph over the next twenty years. The severe storms that have devastated Britain in 1987 and 1990 are part of a cyclical pattern going back at least four centuries, bad storms having occurred at the end of each century for the last 400 years, so we would be well advised to tighten sea and wind defences and batten down our private hatches.

On 25 February 1990, as the storms raged outside, the world's top climatic experts met in Edinburgh to discuss whether the violent changes in climate could be the first alarming results of the man-made greenhouse effect. However, the scientists were nothing if not cautious when it came to committing themselves. Dr Mike Hamilton, of Birmingham University, blamed the gales on natural events, his statement being: 'Some might put this down to global warming. But my advice is to wait and see.' Meteorological office scientist, Dr David Parker, commented: 'A lot more careful research is needed before we can start blaming man for all that is happening.'[4] On the other hand, Dr Jean Palutikov, of the Climatic Research Unit of the University of East Anglia, was happy to deliver a weather forecast for the next 125,000 years, complete with accompanying graph. As reported in the *Daily Telegraph* (22 August 1990), Dr Palutikov suggested that warming due to the greenhouse effect may moderate the result of the next Ice Age. The research in question is being carried out for the nuclear waste executive, Nirex, which is interested in long-term climatic predictions for its research into a multi-billion pound deep underground national waste repository. Since human life began, ice ages, produced by shifts in the Earth's axis in relation to the sun and other celestial bodies in the solar system, have been responsible for some of the greatest natural climatic variations. According to Dr Palutikov, the next glaciation may be moderated by the greenhouse effect, so that Britain will not be engulfed by extensive ice-sheets, as it has been in the distant past.

Drops in sea level, as much as 50 to 70 metres, are also predicted, the predictions taking into account the influence of the greenhouse effect and changes in the Earth's orbit over 100,000 years. Shorter-term influences were outlined as follows:

> Over 41,000 years the orbit can shift the timing of the seasons.
> Over 22,000 years the tilt of the axis of the Earth can vary.
> Other factors, such as the height of mountains and the position of the continents, are also important.
> These variations can lead to seasonal and regional change in the amount of solar heat received by the Earth. This is thought to cause the climate to vary from today's temperate climate to ice age conditions in Britain.
> Greenhouse warming will eventually end once fossil fuel reserves

run out. However, it is possible that the greenhouse effect may influence climate for many thousands of years.

Sunbathers may one day get ultraviolet warnings with the weather forecast if the predicted climate change occurs. Calling for a network of stations to measure ultraviolet radiation, Prof Rona MacKie, of Glasgow University, said: 'If global warming gives Britain a more Mediterranean climate, Britons may benefit from ultraviolet warnings similar to those given in Arizona to prevent skin cancer.'

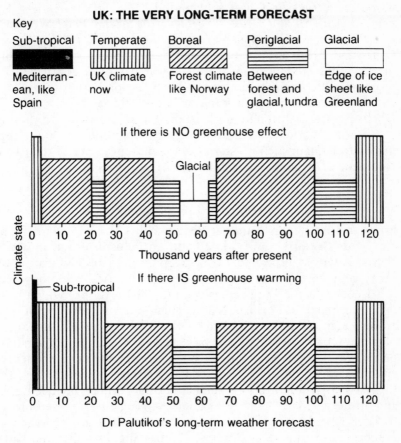

UK: THE VERY LONG-TERM FORECAST

Key

Sub-tropical	Temperate	Boreal	Periglacial	Glacial
Mediterran-ean, like Spain	UK climate now	Forest climate like Norway	Between forest and glacial, tundra	Edge of ice sheet like Greenland

If there is NO greenhouse effect

Glacial

Climate state

Thousand years after present

If there IS greenhouse warming

Sub-tropical

Dr Palutikof's long-term weather forecast

Cycles of Catastrophe

Different cycles have been cited by other scientists. Professor D. Nalivkin, of the Soviet Academy of Science, for example, commented:

Observations of catastrophic phenomena are limited by the time span of no longer than 4,000–6,000 years. For geological processes this is a

short period and it is quite possible that some of the most terrible
catastrophes have not been recorded in the chronicles of mankind. . .
We must not fit into modern standards all that has happened on the
Earth throughout . . . its existence.[5]

Further information on previous axis tilts that have caused dramatic
changes in the Earth's climate, and therefore exerted both long-
and short-term effects on its inhabitants are to be found in the
works of Professor Charles Hapgood: *Maps of the Ancient Sea
Kings, Earth's Shifting Crust, The Path of the Pole*, in Peter Warlow's
The Reversing Earth and also in Jeffrey Goodman's *The Earthquake
Generation*. From a scientific viewpoint Hapgood's work probably
merits more credence, since much of it has been confirmed by
recent satellite pictures indicating clearly, among other things, the
paths of former rivers in what are now arid lands, the flow of
which suggest a different angle of the Earth in relation to the sun
and moon. Warlow, a research physicist, presents his 'tippe top'
theory to explain such mysteries as the disappearance of the island
continent of Atlantis, so vividly described by Plato.

Primitive Time-keepers

From stone carvings found at Pierres Folles, La Filouzière, Ven-
die, and Brittany, and identified as prehistoric astronomical
charts, it would appear that time-keeping predates civilization by
many centuries. Thousands of lines, dots, vertical notations, and
other coherent markings engraved on stone or bone, which have
been ascribed to the Azilian, Magdalenian and Aurignacian cultures,
are also believed to be associated with the recording of time. Some
of these, which are said to date back as far as the Upper Palaeolithic
period (*c.* 35,000 BC) to 8000 BC, accord with time sequences
enumerated in the mythology and sacred writings of the world's
earliest known civilizations such as those of India, ancient Egypt
and Sumeria. Many of these strange markings bear a resemblance
to later Scandinavian runic scripts in that they are arranged as
notches on a foot-rule. Andrew Tomas suggests that the runic
calendar of the Baltic basin may be the grandchild of the prehistoric
notational system. He tells us:

'Dr. L. E. Maistrov of the U.S.S.R. has the opinion that the runic
calendar is based on the solar cycle of 28 years. The begining of this
calendrical system goes back to the year 4713 B.C. . . . To develop a
chronology requires a knowledge of astronomy and mathematics,
accumulated during the course of long ages.[6]

This information would appear to be borne out in the myths and legends of the ancient Frisians, recent borings in the North Sea having established their original lands off the Scandinavian coast to have sank *c.* 5000 BC.

Astrological and Mythical Ages

The Great Year is the name given to the period of time (roughly 25,826 years) taken by the pole of the Earth's axis to complete an entire circle around the ecliptic, which is the sun's apparent path among the stars when viewed against the background of the constellations. The gradual changing of direction in space of the Earth's axis is known as the precession of the equinoxes. Each year the point in space where the sun crosses the celestial equator – referred to by astronomers as the vernal equinox, and by astrologers as Aries – is seen from the Earth as slightly behind the position it occupied the previous year, when viewed against the background of the constellations. Consequently, the nearest star to which the axis points, known as the Pole Star, changes through the ages. Some 4000–5000 years ago the North Pole pointed to Alpha Draconis, whereas it now points to Ursa Minor.

Confusion arises from the fact that the constellations have the same names as the signs of the zodiac. Astronomers, therefore, tend to look askance when those interested but untutored in the subtleties of astrology speak of being 'born under the star sign of Leo' for example. The signs of the zodiac (the word 'zodiac' comes from the Greek and means 'circle of animals') are not synonymous with the constellations with which they share a name, a fact that should be borne in mind when one is thinking of astrological ages. The constellations that are marked on a stellar chart as groups of stars are purely points of reference, since the light of these stars may have taken hundreds of light-years to reach us, and have long since moved to different locations. At the time when these constellations were named, the section of the ecliptic starting from the point of the vernal equinox was called Aries, and the constellation that appeared in its background was also called Aries. Each 30 degrees of ecliptic known are counted from the vernal equinox, and the equinox is slightly farther back each year in relation to the other constellations.

The Great Year

Just as our year is divided into twelve months, the Great Year is similarly divided into twelve ages. These are the periods of time when the equinox is judged as being against the background of each of the twelve constellations that appear to lie roughly around the ecliptic. We are told that these periods cannot be reckoned with any real degree of accuracy, but are roughly 2000 or so years each. Nor can the commencement of each period be fixed, because the boundaries of the constellations are not clearly defined. As the movement is backward from the end of the constellation to its beginning, the periods of time are in a backward order through the signs. The last 2000 years are seen by astrologers to have exhibited characteristics that are decidedly Piscean, while the previous 2000-year period was clearly Arien, and the 2000 preceding that was unmistakably Taurean. Working backwards in this way, we can trace the ages through Gemini to Cancer and Leo, which, according to ancient zodiacs, appeared to play key roles in Gaia's last major quantum leap. Each age is seen as exerting certain psychological influences that manifest strongly in those civilizations which flourish under its ethos. In the ancient Egyptian religion, a Neter (or god) is allotted to each of these periods. The characteristics associated with the divinity in question are mirrored either negatively or positively in the people of those times, according to their stages of somatic evolution and spiritual maturity. According to the astrological experts, we are now just about to enter the Aquarian age, with all that that implies astrologically. (See Glossary.)

The Four Ages of Ancient Greece

The ancient Greeks also viewed certain 'ages' as having relevancy in the growth and evolution of *Homo sapiens*. These they named the Golden Age, Silver Age, Brazen or Bronze Age, and Iron Age respectively. The latter encompassed our present age, for which Hesiod apparently had little regard. These would be impossible to date precisely, but a study of the development of civilization from the following table renders them easily identifiable:

Palaeolithic, or Old Stone Age, designating the cultural period beginning with the earliest chipped stone tools about 2.5–5 million years ago until the beginning of the *Mesolithic* or Middle Stone Age – c. 12,000 years ago.
Neolithic, or New Stone Age – of or defining the cultural period between 12,000 BC–7000 BC in the Middle East and later elsewhere, characterized by the development of farming and the making of technically advanced, polished stone implements.

Chalcolithic – a period in man's development when both stone and copper were in use.
Bronze Age, which brought the Stone Age to an end, is distinguished by the invention of bronze, c. 3000 BC
Iron Age, which followed the Bronze Age, typified by the spread of iron tools and beginning in the Middle East around the twelfth century BC and in Europe about the eighth century BC.

From the aforegoing the Bronze Age of the Greeks is easy to place, while the Silver Age, which could be seen to correspond with the period of matriarchy in Europe, probably flourished between 8000 and 6000 BC – the astrological Age of Cancer. It is at the Golden Age, however, that science and metaphysics part company, the former viewing it as nothing more than Greek fable, and the latter relating it to a highly advanced civilization that is believed to have flourished between 14,000 BC and 8000 BC, (side by side with the Stone Age), to which Plato referred in the *Timaeus* and *Critias*.

Babylonian Astronomy

The Babylonian astronomer and historian Berosus was certainly familiar with the Great Year and the precession of equinoxes; the Sumerians, from whom the Babylonians inherited their knowledge, were the first to give names to the zodiacal figures. Their surviving records indicate that they possessed a much wider understanding of celestial phenomena than any succeeding culture up to recent years. As was the case with many other priestly early cultures, however, their most profound truths were inevitably garbed with the cloak of secrecy so as to render them incoprehensible to the uninitiated.

The Sirius Factor

The ancient Egyptians possessed solar, lunar and Sothic calendars. The Sothic calendar, which was based on the rising of the binary star Sirius (Sothis), featured strongly in their earliest history. The Alsatian Egyptologist and philosopher, R. A. Schwaller de Lubicz, made a detailed study of the Sothic cycle and came up with some very interesting facts:

The Sothic cycle is established on the coincidence every 1,460 years of the *vague year* of 365 days with the *Sothic* (or *Siriun*) *year* of 365¼ days. All civil acts were dated according to the vague year, composed of exactly 360 days plus the five epagomenal days consecrated to the *Neters*: Osiris, Isis, Seth, Nephthys and Horus.

The Siriun or *fixed year*, was established according to the heliacal rising of Sirius, yet the interval between two heliacal risings of Sirius corresponds neither to the tropical year, which is shorter, nor to the sidereal year, which is longer. For it is remarkable that *owing to the precession of the equinoxes, on the one hand, and the movement of Sirius on the other, the position of the sun with respect to Sirius is displaced in the same direction, almost exactly to the same extent.*

Calculations established by astronomers have demonstrated that between 4231 and 2231 BC, the approximate duration of the reign of the Bull *Hap*, the Siriun year was almost identical to our Julian year of 365¼ days. This period would cover the entire Ancient Empire, 'and we cannot but admire the greatness of a science capable of discovering such a coincidence because *Sirius is the only star among the "fixed stars" which allows this cycle.* It can therefore be supposed that Sirius plays the role of a center for the circuit of our entire solar system.'[7]

The Pharaonic calendar is established as being introduced in 4240 BC. The five epagomenal days are related to the birth of the five Neters (astrological ages within the Great Year?), and since the whole arrangement revolves around Sirius, the only star to return periodically every 365¼ days, the inference would be that the cycles of linear time relevant to the Earth, and all that evolves thereon, are somehow orchestrated from the region of the binary star we know as Sirius. Schwaller de Lubicz certainly appears to have arrived at this conclusion and his beliefs in the Siriun influence are expressed in his words:

> The double star of Sirius – which for Pharaonic Egypt played the role of central sun to our entire solar system – today suggests the existence of a cosmic system of atomic structure whose *nucleus* is this 'Great Provider', the Sothis [*spd. t*] of the ancients. There might well be a need to revise our cosmology in the not-so-distant future.[8]

Schwaller de Lubicz also sees Sirius as having some bearing on the climate of our planet and comments on the fact that climatological variation, if only a few degrees, can affect all of life on Earth. A drop in temperature drives people towards other less hostile zones, while warmer temperatures witness the birth of new plant and animal life. Some of the principal movements within our solar system are well known, others not so, and since climatological modifications appear to obey variations in the sidereal year, he regards Sirius as being responsible for both our climate and that of the entire solar system.

There is a school of thought that subscribes to the theory that the number of days in the year was once 360, the five epagomenal days that make up our year having been acquired during a prehistoric axis tilt when the orbit of the Earth in relation to the sun was slightly altered. (Since this discussion constitutes a study in itself, I would recommend the interested reader to my books *Atlantis: Myth or Reality?* or *Ancient Egypt: The Sirius Connection*, both of which cover the subject in considerably more detail and provide reference material for further study.)

In more recent years, the significance of Sirius, as far as human evolution is concerned, was studied and amplified by the internationally renowned mathematician and philosopher Dr Charles Arthur Musès, whose work in science and pure mathematics has led to published studies on higher algebra, modern physics, cybernetics and the nature of time. In a more popular work, *The Lion Path*, he has set out to apply his scientific expertise to the role of time resonances, including those of Sirius, in Gaia's affairs.

He discussed particularly an evolutionary quantum leap, which, it is believed, will be set in motion through noetic energies resonant with Sirius and its white dwarf companion. In *The Lion Path* he has some new things to say regarding   (a) the space-time role of the planets in our solar system, including two that are not as yet generally known and   (b) the significance of the Sirius system to the future of humanity. His emphasis on Sirius, and the significance of time waves as an operative force in our future, may prove of interest to those who prefer cogent grounds for their metaphysical concepts by someone of qualification and distinction in the academic field.

Regarding (a), he supports the idea that there are twelve time-influencing bodies in our solar system. In addition to the familiar Saturn, Jupiter, Mars, Sun, Venus, Mercury, Moon, Uranus, Neptune and Pluto, he cites Pan and Vulcan:[9]

> Pan is the perturbationally indicated outermost planet of our solar system, with a perihelion just outside the aphelion of Pluto that is to say, an orbit completely enclosing that of Pluto. Vulcan, already named by Neptune's discoverer, the great astronomer Leverrier, is the single infra-Mercurial planet of our system which was later denied by astronomers but which is shown to lie at a mean distance of 0.24 astronomical units (one such unit being the mean distance of the Earth from the Sun) and to have a period of 43 days. There is only one Bessel function zero closer than the first zero of the first order, and that is the first zero of the zeroth order, corresponding to the infra-Mercurial Planet Vulcan.

He sees Sirius, the brightest star in our heavens, as the macro-cosmic seat of transformative energies that are transmitted to

Earth via space-time waves resonant with the twelve above-mentioned celestial bodies, in what one would imagine to be much the same way that energy is released and transferred in microcosmic quantum fields. Then those of humankind who are able to resonate with those energies and employ them correctly can gain mastery over the element of Time in their lives and evolution, and help lead humanity out of its current morass of political and environmental collision courses. This is the message.

Dr. Musès' major work on Time, which is highly technical, although its key Chapters 3 and 5 can be read by any intelligent lay person, is *Destiny and Control in Human Systems*, subtitled 'Studies in the Interactive Connectedness of Time (Chronotopology)'. (See Bibliography.)

The Vedic Yugas

The Vedas of Hinduism, which are considered to be the oldest Indian documents, represent the religion of the Aryans who invaded the subcontinent over the period from 1400 to 500 BC. One of the main teachings of Vedism is that the course of the universe through time is cyclical. Every event has occurred before and will occur again. This theory applies not only to the life of the individual in the course of his or her rebirths but also to the history of society, the lives of the gods, and the evolution of the entire cosmos.

In Hindu cosmology the smallest units of time involved in this cosmic cycle are the *yugas* or world ages. There are four of these, each of which is progressively shorter and represents a diminution of the total dharma, or moral order, of the universe. They are named *kritā* (also spelled *krtā*), *tretā, dvāpara* and *kali* respectively. The *kritā yuga*, or era of perfection is 1,728,000 years in duration; the *tretā yuga*, in which the dharma is reduced by one quarter, is three quarters as long, 1,296,000 years; in the *dvāpara yuga*, dharma is reduced to one half, and its length is only 864,000 years. The final era, or *kali yuga*, in which the dharma is reduced to one quarter, lasts for only 432,000 years. The *kali yuga*, which encompasses our own era, is believed to have commenced on Friday, 18 February, 3102 BC. According to the Vedic teachings, the closing years of the *kali yuga* will be characterized by the breakdown of social classes, the end of worship, and disrespect for scripture, sages, and moral standards. When these degradations reach their peak the *yuga* will end with flood, fire and war. Then the entire cycle of four *yugas*, known as the *mahāyuga*, or great *yuga*, will begin again to unfold for another 4,320,000 years.

One thousand *mahāyugas* – 4,320,000,000 years – constitute a *kalpa*, a single day in the life of the god Brahma. At the end of each such day all matter in the universe is reabsorbed into the universal spirit, and during the night of Brahma, also one *kalpa* in length, matter persists only as potential for reappearance. At each dawn Brahma re-emerges from a lotus, which grows from the naval of the god Vishnu, and matter is formed again. The present age is the first day of the fifty-first year of Brahma. The year is made up of 360 days and nights. Brahma lives for 100 years, after which a total dissolution of the universe occurs and all spheres of being become without existence to remain thus for another Brahma century. Finally, Brahma is reborn, and the immense cycle lasting for 311,040,000,000,000 years begins anew.

Here we would appear to have a perfect description of what is currently referred to as the Big Bang. The early years in the life of this phenomenal universal creation reflect the glory of order, after which entropy commences to take its slow but inevitable toll, leading eventually to chaos and final disintegration – the Big Crunch. The matter/antimatter sequence indicated by our previously illustrated sine-wave theory would certainly seem to fit this concept, which, in the microcosmic context could be seen to parallel with the birth/maturity/ageing process to which mankind, like all other life forms within the universe, is subject.

Biological Rhythms

Just as celestial bodies appear to function according to some cyclic pattern, while also negotiating both the orderly and chaotic modes, so the human body also responds to certain rhythms which are determined by lunar, solar and other external forces. Notable among these are the circadian rhythms (from the Latin *circa*, about and *dies*, day) that pertain to the endogenous or exogenous (internal and external) processes that exhibit approximately 24-hour periodicity. Although people living close to nature have been aware of these natural cycles for centuries, concrete evidence acceptable to the scientific community did not find its way into publication until 1729, when the French astronomer Jean de Mairan detected the regular cycles of the *Mimosa pudica*. Since then, numerous examples of 24-hour long rhythms have been noted, and their synchronization with natural rhythm duly observed. In recent years the jet-lag phenomenon has more than confirmed how we humans are as much influenced by our biological clocks as the insects, animals and plants.

The 24-hour cycle is only one, however, there are also the complex lunar rhythms which women would seem to be more prone to follow. The human female menstrual cycle, for example, shares an approximation with the lunar month of 29.6 days, although it is worth mentioning at this point that not all women respond to the lunar cycle. I know of several whose body-clocks are tuned to the solar rhythms, but that constitutes the subject matter of another study. Many plants and insects respond to lunar energies, which are also responsible for the tidal cycles that bring about the variations of temperature, pressure and wave disturbance so essential to the breeding habits and routines of many minute marine life forms. Such rhythms are driven by endogenous clocks.

Scientists inform us that the biochemical mechanisms of circadian clocks are still unknown, although new information is continually emerging. For example, there is evidence that the circadian rhythm is not the product of a single clock, but rather of a series of complex organisms that unite to produce one particular pulse which is actually a 25-hour cycle. What happens is that the body adjusts its mechanisms through a process known as 'entrainment', which has been likened to regularly adjusting a watch that gains a set amount of time each day.[10] This natural adjustment of the body-clock from the 25- to the 24-hour cycle was proven empirically in 1972 by the French cave explorer Michel Siffre, who spent seven months living alone in the Midnight Cave near Del Rio in Texas. Although he carried out regular periods of rest and activity without natural light to guide his body-clock, he assumed the 25-hour cycle with comfort.

All this rather suggests that there might well have been a time in the distant, prehistoric past when there were 25 hours in a day and not the 24 to which we have become accustomed. In keeping with the calendar makers, who saw to it that the five epagomenal days were comfortably absorbed, the human body effected its own adjustments. Siffre went on to organize a further experiment that involved Jacques Chabert and Phillipe Englander, who entered separate caves in the south of France in mid-August 1968 and emerged on 15 January 1969. Both had estimated the date of their surfacing to be 15 November 1968. Relying only on their biological clocks, they had dropped two months behind.[11]

Not all plants and animals share the same circadian rhythms as humankind, however, and biological clocks ranging from 22 to 28 hours have been identified and recorded. Light would certainly seem to be the prime factor involved in the rhythms adopted by these various biological clocks, and recent studies have yielded up a wealth of information on the subject. Coveney and Highfield tell us:

> Franz Halberg has used computer analysis to tease out some of the details of body rhythms and has found that they cover a number of tempi. He likes to compare the discovery of this spectrum of rhythms with the discovery by Newton in 1666 that white light can be carved up into a spectrum of colours by a prism. Just as we use the terms ultraviolet and infrared to describe radiation at either end of the visible part of the electromagnetic spectrum, so Halberg refers to 'ultradian' and 'infradian' to describe cycles shorter and longer than the circadian period. In nature the ultradian notes are played by the nervous system, where oscillations may only last one-tenth of a second, moving down in frequency as we encounter heart beats at around one cycle per second and breathing at one cycle every four seconds, to longer hormonal and metabolic oscillations, and on to the 24-hour cycle, the middle C of the biological ensemble which even seems to rule our sense of timekeeping. [12]

Our circadian rhythms are, we are informed, encoded in specific genes, so one could say that they are predetermined prior to our birth. However, it is possible to reprogramme them mentally. I have tried this myself, especially on flights of 24 hours or longer, and it does work. While on the subject of jet-lag. I have also heard it said that flying from east to west causes less of a problem to the circadian rhythms, whereas I myself have found exactly the opposite. Disturbed sleep, alterations in body temperature, hormone cycles and shift work are all seen as enemies of our natural rhythms. It always amazes me how some people can stay up all night and sleep until noon the following day, whereas people like me, whose rhythms are strongly influenced by the solar cycle, are unable to cope with nightly activity or sleep during daylight (unless ill) without getting a nasty headache.

Scientists have now confirmed the age-old belief that the pineal gland plays a vital role in the machinery that governs our master clock. This is something metaphysicians have long been aware of, although until recent years they lacked the backing of empirical research to state the case for their belief. The pineal gland is a small, reddish vascular body in the posterior part of the third ventricle of the brain. Until recently its function in *Homo sapiens* was uncertain, although in animals it is known to secrete a substance known as 'melatonin'. Recent research has come to link it with the effect of light and seasonal variations on the bodily functions. Seasonal depressions are believed to have pineal origins, while the pigment melatonin is associated with skin colour. To the ancients it was the 'third eye', described by René Descartes once as 'the place where the soul exercises influence over the body'.[13] It is now known to be light-sensitive and have many features in common with the retina, and via the action of the melatonin it secretes it provides vital information on the regular cycles of time on this planet – night and day, and the seasons. The pineal gland is also responsible for thermo-regulation (body temperature) and for various moods we may encounter.

A study of the effect of ancient seasonal rites would certainly prove fruitful to those scientists engaged in the analysis of pineal functions in humans. These rites were mainly designed to stimulate the pineal gland so as to effect the individual's adjustment to the oncoming season. Thus, one aspect of the mental and physical health of the tribe could be ensured for the ensuing months. Ritual, like the various forms of mind-programming that are becoming increasingly popular, can exert a considerable influence over the autonomic nervous system, the brain, the mental system and the endocrine system. When used wisely and under expert guidance these programming (or self-programming, as the case may be) systems can prove of benefit to many, but the dangers arise when they are employed without training or prior knowledge of the mental and biological mechanics involved. (See Hope, *The Psychology of Ritual*).

The study of ancient monuments and megaliths has supplied sufficient evidence to suggest that the patterns of solar and lunar cycles, and their effect on all life forms was certainly understood by the people who erected them. The sun's cycle involves its rising further north on the horizon each day from mid-winter to mid-summer, after which it reverses to rise and set a little further in the south each day until the next mid-winter. The moon's rising and setting, however, does not follow such a precise annual pattern, although it rises more to the north on some days and more to the south on others; the cycle repeats itself from the viewpoint of Earth over a period of 18.61 years. Gribbin draws our attention to the fact that: 'The nearest whole number of years that can be fitted reasonably well to this lunar rhythm is 56 years, the time it takes for the cycle to repeat three times. That number, too, had significance for the builders of Stonehenge. . .'[14] But this is the subject of another study: those interested are referred to Dr Gribbin's book, *Timewarps*.

I have no doubt that the pineal gland acts as a gateway between Inner and Outer Time, and that certain prehistoric civilizations were well aware of this. It would be interesting if a scientific study of those people who are able to experience multidimensional awareness, or who possess the ability to time travel mentally, could be effected in relation to neurohormonal functioning. I have a feeling that our scientists would find some interesting facts for future research papers: the shamanic 'heat' effect, for example, the changes experienced in the autonomic nervous system during altered states of consciousness involving experiences in Outer Time or dreams that involve trips to parallel universes – but more of that later.

Time and Evolution

'Deep geological time' is the term applied to what we now know to be the real age of the Earth, as against the various guesses and religious surmises our forefathers were conditioned to believe for so many years. The measurement of radioactive decay added more noughts to the figure, and we now find ourselves facing the fact that we live on a moving body which existed for billions of years prior to the evolution of our particular species. Deep time is often seen as being a hard concept to grasp and, taking into account the estimated age of Gaia, our period of habitation on her body could be viewed as *less* than a *minute* in a 24-hour day of linear time. And yet it took all of those aeons to produce an environment suitable for our habitation, that is if you subscribe to the belief (which I do not) that Gaia spent all that time preparing herself for the sole purpose of accommodating mankind. Many species have come and gone over the period since life as we know it first emerged from the primeval swamps and, as Professor Sir James Lovelock so succinctly puts it, we could well be the next lot of dinosaurs to be ejected if we continue to assault out planetary host. It is as simple as that.

So, what role does time play in our evolution and that of those other species that have drawn their sustenance from the bosom of Gaia since she was born? In using the term 'species' I am not limiting my reference to those denizens of the real world that we have come to acknowledge as 'living', but also to the original elemental and microorganic energies that prepared the surface of our planet for each successive stage in its evolutionary development. In all of this time has played a primary role. How many million years did we say went by before we were hatched? It is natural for us to think in terms of a year, as we now know it. But what if there were, for vast periods of time, 'years' that were composed of a different number of months and days; what if the moon, for example, was situated just a little nearer, or further out from its present position, and the angle of the Earth to the sun rendered its natural rhythms somewhat different from what they are today?

Over these vast periods Gaia provided a bed of experience for all kinds of intelligences, (if one subscribes to the idea that all living things are motivated by some external factor, be it an organizing group entity or an individual mind or consciousness). According to the evolutionists, microorganisms and bacteria formed the basis of life as we recognize it, and as such did the groundwork essential to the future growth of the elements of which our bodies ultimately came to be formed. We still host many of these bacteria and rely on them for a balanced state of health.

In a recorded television interview, James Lovelock spoke of the age and evolution of Gaia and dwelt at some length on the various life forms that go to regulate her body – our planet. Among the many facts he told his viewers concerning the nature of Gaia, his statement that 'any species noxious to those around it will be destroyed or destroy itself' struck me as highly significant. Humanity, he believes, has broken the rules and has so far managed to get away with it, but if we continue to prove destructive to Gaia we are expendable, as Gaia will resist any changes that do not accord with her own evolutionary pattern. Algae and trees help Gaia to condition and regulate her body and keep it in good health. Although she may have experienced the odd assault from outer space in times distant, a blow from a planetesimal (small extraterrestrial body), for example, would not kill her.

As Gaia adjusts her body to accommodate her personal spiritual growth, variations in the positions of poles and equator may cause lands to rise and fall, oceans to cover what were formerly arid lands, and fertile plains to become ice-bound for centuries, in much the same way that a wise farmer will plant wheat one year and cabbages the next, followed by a year of rest to enable the soil to replenish its nutrients and effect a natural rebalance. Lovelock commented on how we in our selfishness see everything in terms of our own wants and conveniences, whereas Gaia tends to view what takes place on her body in more holistic terms. It is not the plants, trees, animals, bacteria or algae that contaminate her surface; the real pollution, says Lovelock, is *people*!

Lovelock also referred to the dark side to Gaia. This is interesting since, according to the myths, retribution was inevitably dispensed by avenging goddesses, who were nothing if not ruthless in their punishment of transgressors. And if the various names accorded to these deities by the great civilizations of the past are no more than the many names of Gaia, then we should surely heed their message. An interesting corollary to all this is that the goddesses of destruction and regeneration are, according to the ancients, inevitably bound up with the gods of time, a subject I will be dealing with in the next chapter.

If time does exist in stationary bands through which we pass, as Lyall Watson has suggested, then surely evolution is inextricably bound up with the time factor, or the band of time through which this planet has passed or is still passing. Could it be that with each quantum leap Gaia is removed to a different time-band, so that with the change of frequencies our evolution could take a new turn of direction, or even cease at that point, as was the case with the dinosaurs? It bears consideration. But to return to our so-termed 'real world' and the evolutionary plan as presented by Darwin. Nobel laureate Salvador Luria might have had a point when he wrote:

> Evolution, like history, is not like coin-tossing or a game of cards. It has another essential characteristic: irreversibility. All that will be is the descendant of what is, just as what is comes from what has been, not from what might have been. Men are the children of reality, not of hypothetical situations, and evolutionary reality – the range of organisms that actually exist – is but a small sample of all past opportunities. [15]

The increasing complexity of biological evolution is seen as a firm indication that it is a time-directed process, and therefore provides confirmation for the arrow of time emphasized by Coveney and Highfield.

The aforegoing gives rise to several points, however. Luria's statement certainly holds good when applied to evolution as we know it on this planet. But the fact that time's arrow of irreversibility would seem to pertain to our linear time (which I do not dispute) should not be taken as proof that there are no parallel universes that also involve Gaia, in which we and other life forms, which have utilized her body for experience at this particular level of matter, may well have effected different, perhaps kinder and more sober decisions regarding the employment of her facilities.

Anyway, the idea of a time-directed process, in the scientific context, does appear to suggest some master plan or 'mind' behind it all, or are we dealing once more with the randomness of chaos? The religious person would naturally suggest that 'God' had a hand in it all, while the metaphysician would broaden this horizon to include a variety of 'powers' – gods, godlings, Neters, and so forth. Besides, not all researchers are of the opinion that mankind appeared on this planet by evolutionary design, Richard Mooney, for example, who conceives of *Homo sapiens* as an imported species, which premise he supports with some questionable, albeit unusual, evidence.[16]

What probably happens is that different time-circuits or bands carry different emphases or impulses, and it is the nature of the time-impulse through which a planet travels at a *particular frequency* that is the deciding factor as to whether monkeys, cats, lizards or insects eventually evolve to become the dominant species on its surface. (My italics refer to my belief that all universes exist on more than one frequency, so that no experience is ever repeated, but more of this in Part 2.)

Difficult to believe though it may be, there are still schools of religious thought that deny our simian ancestry. However, genetic fingerprinting has now presented us with some substantial evidence which supports Darwin's original premise. Only one per cent of our DNA differs from that of the chimpanzees although, in evolutionary terms, we stand at some distance from our hairy cousins. In the late 1980s, Morris Goodman, of Wayne State University, proposed that humans, chimps and gorillas be placed in the same new sub-family, *Homininae*, instead of leaving humans in proud isolation in their own classification. There are two branches of the chimpanzee family, however, the common chimp and the pygmy chimp, both of which are more closely related to humans than they or we humans are to anything else, including the gorilla. Jared Diamond, of the University of California, Los Angeles (UCLA), proposed that the correct classification would be three types of chimpanzee – common, pygmy and human. The gorilla line split off from the chimpanzee line between eight and eleven million years ago, the split between our own genus and the chimps having occurred a little over five million years ago.[17]

The eternal question is, of course, what caused that split, and why did two sections of the chimp genus stay as they were, while the third one engaged in a biological evolutionary quantum leap? One must assume that when any species moving through the circuits of one of time's stationary bands strikes a given point that would equate with a quantum leap, there will be those among its members that will respond to that impulse, and those that will be insufficiently sensitive to register its significance either mentally or somatically. Let us take a class of children as an example.

For several terms they have been instructed by the same tutor; some have absorbed their lessons with moderate ease, others have either paid no attention or were unable to grasp what they were being taught, while a few have mastered the principles quickly and therefore find the remainder of term somewhat boring. Half-way through the term circumstances oblige the regular teacher to abandon her post and a new, and more highly qualified one comes to take her place. Her pace of teaching is considerably faster and more inspiring than that of her predecessor, and as a result the bright pupils shoot ahead, while those of moderate intelligence manage to keep abreast with the tuition by undertaking home-work or extramural studies. But the slower ones, who were already lagging behind, become quite lost and are unable to pass the necessary end-of-term exams that would enable them to move up to the next class.

This scenario applied in the Gaia context might provide a clue as to the sudden (and for all we know unprecedented) demise of the dinosaurs. In fact, viewing time in terms of an energy can supply the answers to many evolutionary enigmas that have baffled mankind for centuries and still provide fuel for scientific debate.

Endnotes

1. P. Coveney and R. Highfield, *The Arrow of Time*, p. 264.
2. M. Gauquelin, *Cosmic Clocks*, p. 105.
3. A. Tomas, *We are Not the First*, p. 96.
4. The *Daily Mail* 26 February 1990.
5. C. Berlitz, *Atlantis*, pp. 193–4.
6. Tomas, *op. cit.*, p. 79–80.
7. R. A. Schwaller de Lubicz, *Sacred Science*, pp. 26–7.
8. *Ibid*. p. 28.
9. Musaios, *The Lion Path*, p. 60.
10. Coveney and Highfield, *The Arrow of Time,* p. 302.
11. A. Tomas, *Beyond the Time Barrier*, p. 24.
12. Coveney and Highfield, *op. cit.*, p. 303.
13. *Ibid*. p. 309.
14. J. Gribbin, *Timewarps*, p. 9.
15. Coveney and Highfield, *op. cit.* p. 254.
16. R. Mooney, *Colony: Earth* and *Gods of Air and Darkness*.
17. J. Gribbin and M. Gribbin, the *Guardian* (14 June 1988).

Part 2

Abstractions and Conclusions

6
Time in Myth, History and Religion

The wise remember the past and understand the future, but the ignorant live only for the fleeting pleasures of the present.
ZOROASTER[1]

Those who consider the study of space-time to be the prerogative of the modern day are grossly mistaken. Mankind has ever been obsessed with time, and during the early phases of our history the time concept was conveyed to the illiterate by the erudite in the same way as most other abstract principles by way of myth, legend or parable. Somewhere in the far distant past people must have been aware of the nature of time as an energy, since they chose to accord it a divine identity in much the same way that they personalized other natural forces or energies. The earliest hint we have of this comes from ancient Sumerian and Egyptian sources where, it is interesting to note, most of the gods of time were inevitably lunar deities.

Sumeria/Babylonia

An ancient text tells the story of the descent of Inanna, the Sumerian queen of heaven and earth, to the 'Great Below' wherein dwells her sister, Ereshkigal, who is queen of those dark regions. Inanna was the daughter of the moon god, Sîn, who also features prominently in Babylonian myth. Sîn and his wife Ningal (Great Lady, who could be equated with the Egyptian Nut), had three children; the Sumerian goddess Inanna, also known as Ishtar and associated with the energies of the planet Venus, the god Shamash, who represented the sun, and Nusku, the god of fire, although a later version sees Inanna as having a 'dark twin' in the person of Ereshkigal. Sîn had many functions, not the least of which was the measuring of time, which serves to connect him

103

with that other male lunar deity, the Egyptian Thoth, who was also a 'time lord'.

In his physical aspect Sîn was also venerated at Ur under the name of Nannar and represented as an old man, with a long beard the colour of lapis lazuli, who normally wore a turban. Each evening he entered his barque (the crescent moon) and navigated the vast spaces of the nocturnal sky. However, according to the legend, 'one day the crescent gave way to a disk which stood in the sky like a gleaming crown'[2] and thenceforth Sîn was known as 'Lord of the Diadem'. Sîn's role as measurer of time had apparently been decided by Marduk, god of fertility, on the day of creation:

> At the month's beginning to shine on earth
> Thou shalt show two horns to mark six days.
> On the seventh day divide the crown in two;
> On the fourteenth day, turn thy full face.[3]

The cosmological connotations here are easy to identify. Through the energies of time, the sun, its fiery brother (whose planetary identity is obscure, assuming he originally had one), and the planet Venus, were created, followed later by Venus' dark twin or sister planet (Earth?). In keeping with most ancient myths and traditions, Earth is shown as a dark or fallen place or, as I would prefer to put it, a planet that has somehow become 'out of its time'. One phrase that particularly caught my eye, however, was 'one day the crescent gave way to a disk'. Are we to assume from this that up to a certain point in time the moon had not manifested as a whole sphere? I have long suspected that the moon did not always occupy its present position in our skies, and that from the time it commenced to so do mankind's concept of time also changed; hence the association of time with the lunar gods of antiquity.

Egypt

Next we come to the most famous of all time lords, the Egyptian Tehuti, latterly known as Thoth. And once again the moon features strongly in the time saga. Of Thoth, the famous Egyptologist E. A. Wallis Budge had this to say:

> . . . he made the calculations concerning the stabilising of the heavens, and the stars, and the earth, that he was the heart of Ra, that he was the master of law both in its physical and moral conceptions, and that he had the knowledge of 'divine speech'. From many passages we see that he was the inventor and god of all arts and sciences, that he was 'lord of books', and the 'scribe of the gods' . . .[4]

Most famous of all his exploits, however, was his acquisition of the five epagomenal days. The story goes thus: Shu and Tefnut, the twin lion-gods of time, who were the children of Ra, in turn gave birth to Geb and Nut (Earth and Sky). According to some accounts Nut was the spouse of Ra, whom she offended by her infidelity. As a punishment the old god decreed that she should not be delivered of a child on any of the 360 days of his year, which might have posed a problem for her had not Thoth played his famous game of draughts with the moon, from which he won a seventy-second part of her light (1/72nd of 360 is exactly 5), which he made into five new days known as 'epagomenal', or also called 'intercalary'. Nut was then able to give birth to the five children she had been carrying – Osiris, Horus the Elder, Set, Isis and Nephthys, in that order. This legend is also echoed in the Greek myth of Cronus (Time) swallowing five of his own children and disgorging them after taking a potion administered to him by Metis (Justice).

Although various mystical and magical interpretations have been placed upon these stories by scholars, psychics and romantics, what the myths are basically telling us is that as a result of some cosmological drama played out between the Earth, the moon and some solar energy external to our star system, the calendar had to be changed, and that it was Thoth, a lunar deity, who was responsible for effecting the alteration. In other words, at some point in the distant past there occurred a variation in the Earth's orbital relationship with the moon, precipitating the change in the Earth's axis that was responsible for the acquisition of the five extra days we now have in our calendars. Because, according to ancient Egyptian sources, Sirius was involved in these proceedings, the bright, blue-white binary star in the constellation of Canis Major was probably the third, and perhaps the most influential player in this celestial drama. Thoth is also recognized as the scribe who records the thoughts and deeds of all living things in the timeless annals of 'Akasha'; the significance of this as far as our study of time is concerned is obvious.

All the time gods were not male, however. Two goddesses in the Egyptian pantheon also had temporal associations. These were Seshat and Maat, both of whom, at one period or other were mentioned as being the wives (feminine aspects?) of Thoth. Seshat was a goddess of writing and history, a measurer of time and, like Thoth himself, a Recorder. Maat, on the other hand, was the goddess of truth and justice on whose scales the heart of the deceased was inevitably weighed. Time deities are usually associated with justice and judgement, the inference being that in the final analysis it will be our personal handling of the energies of time that will tip the scales one way or the other.

The twin lion-gods, Shu and Tefnut, were also strongly associated with time. Shu was a sky god who was sometimes portrayed in human form and at others as a lion. His sister Tefnut, who was also shown as leonine, was a goddess of the dew, soft rain and sometimes the rainbow. In fact, the association between lion-gods and time goes back a very long way, the oldest known leonine deity being Aker, who was believed to guard the gate of dawn through which the sun-god passed each morning. From the pyramid texts it is clear that this deity's role and attributes were clearly defined in the early Empire. In later dynasties it was believed that during the night the sun passed through a kind of tunnel which existed in some nether region, each end of which was guarded by a lion-god, the two deities being called Akeru or Akerui. The same leonine divinities later emerged in Theban times as the twin lion-gods of 'yesterday and today', seated back to back, with the sun's disc, representing Ra, supported between them.

Ra was often referred to as 'Ra of the Two Horizons' – 'horizon' being seen by some scholars in this context as a mathematical term denoting a system of dimensions or frame of reference. These were the Light Horizon and the Life Horizon, representing the material worlds and subtle dimensions respectively. Ra, of the Life Horizon, was betokened by a flattened circle or solar disc mounted on the hindquarters of the twin lion-gods.

This symbology has been subjected to several interpretations from the esoteric to the mathematical. For example, some see the two lions as exemplifying the two primordial forces of life – desire and fear – while to others they are simply the past and present united by the sun of the Eternal Now; in other words, the power of time. Their back-to-back position can therefore be interpreted as: (a) the masculine 'desire' force, and the feminine 'fear' force pulling in diferent directions, (chaos?), while the weight of the Ra disc (reason, self-control and order) holds them in check; or (b) in the 'time' context, where the disc can be seen as the solar force that holds our planet in its orbital path and thus creates night and day – the time on our clocks – Inner Time. Should one or both of those lions move their position, even slightly, then the orb of Ra would adjust accordingly and we would see the sun from a *different angle* than we do today. According to ancient Egyptian records, shifts in the Earth's axis, with their accompanying climatic and catastrophic phenomena, are always preceded by a visitation from one of the lion-gods, the goddess Sekhmet being the major harbinger of disasters of this kind. Thus, for the ancient Egyptians anyway, lion symbology and time were inextricably bound together.

The ancient Egyptians also appeared to be aware of the continual swing between the cosmic principles of order and chaos, to which they ascribed recognizable identities. The role played by time in this eternal dual which was seen as having taken place over thousands of years is highlighted in the words of Budge:

> A very early Egyptian tradition made a great fight to take place between the god of light and the god of darkness, and in later days Ra himself, or some form of him, generally one of the Horus gods, was identified with the god of light, and Set, in one form or other, was identified with the god of darkness. Thus the fights of Ra and Apep, and Heru-Behutet and Set, and Horus, son of Isis, and Set, are in reality only different versions of one and the same story, though belonging to different periods. In all these fights Thoth played a prominent part, for when the Eye of Ra, i.e. the Sun, was doing battle with Set, this evil power managed to cast clouds over it, and it was Thoth who swept them away, and 'brought the Eye alive, and whole, and sound, and without defect' to its lord. (*Book of the Dead*, xvii, 71 ff.)[5]

Substitute 'Time' for 'Thoth' in this tale, and assume the other divinities to be personifications of cosmic events, and we will probably find ourselves with a fairly accurate description of the various upheavals that took place on Earth during those prehistoric periods that were doubtless recorded in the annals of some long-lost race that was subsequently relegated to myth and fairy-tale.

North America

The Egyptians were by no means the only race to observe and record intercosmic events that took place in the archaic past. The universality of the symbology associated with alterations in the Earth's axial rotation, for example, may be shown in the Hopi Indian legend of the twin gods Poqanghoya and Palongawhoya, guardians of the north and south axes of the Earth respectively, whose task it was to keep the planet rotating properly. The legend tells how they were ordered by Sotuknang, nephew of the Creator, to leave their posts so that the 'second world' could be destroyed because its people had become evil. Then the world, with no one to control it, teetered off balance, spun around crazily, then rolled over twice. Mountains plunged into the sea with a great splash, seas and lakes sloshed over the land; and as the world spun through cold and lifeless space it froze into solid ice.[6] The Hopi also insist that their 'first world' was destroyed by fire and their 'third world' by water.

Here we have a geologically verifiable folklore account of the massive upheavals that caused mountain ranges such as the Andes to rise, the Ice Age, and the Deluge which received coverage in the myths of many ancient cultures, notably those of Greece, Ireland, Wales, North and South America, Scandinavia, and probably the best known of all, in the Old Testament of the Bible. In other words, the powerful effects of time's energy did not go unnoticed by those who were witness to its fury in ages past, and who generously recorded for posterity the events they observed as our planet plunged through one of the more active 'stationary bands', as defined by Lyall Watson, taking its children with it through the jaws of death.

Rome

The male-orientated cult of Mithras, which was so popular among the Roman Legions, had its own time deity in the lion-headed Aion – 'the boundless "Time", which presides unmoved and unmoving over the entire universe.' Aion holds the two keys to the solsticial gates. In her book *Mystery Religions*, Joscelyn Godwin tells us:

> The silver one is to the Gate of Cancer, 'which leads to the way of the ancestors (Pitri-yana) and to reincarnation. The golden one is to the Gate of Capricorn, the Way of the Gods (Deva-yana) which leads beyond the Circle of Necessity, i.e. to release from the round of birth and death. These are the two routes from which the soul can exit from the world at death, and the Capricorn gate is the one through which the gods descend to earth.'

It was believed that Mithras, in common with other major deities, was born at the time of the winter solstice.

Aion could probably be identified with the Buddhist Shin-je, Judge of the Dead, which would bring him in line with the Egyptian Thoth and other gods of time who are accorded the judgemental role. He is always depicted with a lion's head, and sometimes with four wings and encircled by a serpent, which symbols are seen to represent the fourfold division and cyclic motion of time. In common with other deities of destruction and regeneration Aion's open leonine mouth devours his progeny at the end of each cycle of cosmic manifestation, which reminds us of the Greek Cronus swallowing his children. Several of his symbols have obvious underworld connotations, which emphasizes time's influence over the subatomic regions. In another portrayal he is depicted mounted on a zodiacal-encircled globe and carrying a sceptre on which the zodiacal signs are clearly indicated by twelve divisions. Godwin comments:

> The two bands crossing the globe recall the World Soul's method of creation in Plato's *Timaeus*, by crossing the two circles of world-stuff in the form of an X. Aion is a creator, but not of worlds: he emanates metaphysical principles or gods. In the Persian theogony he is Zervan, whose two sons are the opposites Ormuzd and Ahriman between which Mithras mediates. So he is in a way the highest aspect of Mithras, being beyond rather than between the two opposites.

From the aforegoing, time's influence over the two polar extremes of order and chaos is easily recognizable, and the other point that caught my eye was the reference to Gate of Cancer as being the Way of the Ancestors, since Sirius, which is believed by some to play a major role in the manifestation of time, has its astronomical placing at approximately 13 degrees and 24 minutes of Cancer. Regarding the allusion to the breakaway from the round of birth and death, an explanation of this may be seen in particle-antiparticle discoveries of quantum mechanics, a metaphysical interpretation of which is to be found in Chapters 8 and 9.

Greece

Since the name Cronus means 'time', an examination of the myth of the Greek god Cronus will serve to throw some light on the knowledge possessed by the Greek sages, philosophers and scholars concerning time. Orphic cosmogony, which is considered by many scholars to be far removed from the primitive by virtue of its scientific and philosophic preoccupations and the many abstractions employed in its explanations, tells of Cronus, or Time, being the first principle. Time was, in turn, followed by Chaos, which symbolized the Infinite (Outer Time or timelessness) and Ether, which represented the finite (Inner or linear Time).

Cronus was one of the Titans, or first divine race, whose name derives from the Cretan word meaning 'king'. In Greece, the Titans were ultimately honoured as the ancestors of men, and to them was attributed the invention of the arts and magic. Students of Atlantology (the study of the lost continent of Atlantis) firmly believe that these Titans were the people of lost Atlantis, a highly advanced civilization whose mid-Atlantic island continent ultimately sank during the tilt of the Earth's axis that heralded the arrival of the five epagomenal days, as described in Plato's famous *Timaeus* and *Critias* dialogues.

From the aforegoing, the name 'Cronus' itself, and other evidence from myth and legend, it would be logical to assume that the first calendar was probably of Atlantean origin (the Sothic calendar adopted by the ancient Egyptians, perhaps?), and that these prehistoric people, whoever they might have been, possessed a knowledge of time and the universe comparable or superior to our own.

The legend of Cronus swallowing each of his children as they were born has already received mention, but Time had been up to his old tricks prior to this episode. The first children to be born to Uranus (the Sky) and Gaia (the Earth) were the twelve Titans, six males and six females, of whom Cronus was the youngest son. Their progeny were handsome, clever and presentable, and therefore gave no offence to their parents. But in time Gaia also found herself giving birth to a series of horrendous and misshapen monsters, which so upset her husband that he shut them in the depths of the Earth as soon as they were born. Being a kindly mother, Gaia naturally mourned for her lost children, but in time her sorrow turned to anger and she planned a terrible vengeance against her spouse. Producing a gleaming sickle or *harpe*, she explained her plan to her children, all of whom were horror-struck – except Cronus, who agreed to carry out the dastardly deed. That night, while the unsuspecting Uranus slept, Cronus struck off his father's testicles and cast them into the sea. The message behind the myth tells us of a whole civilization being rendered impotent by time.

We have already discussed how Cronus swallowed his own children. Hestia, Demeter, Hera, Hades and Poseidon were each swallowed in turn, but when Cronus' wife, Rhea, was about to give birth to Zeus, she was so distressed by her husband's behaviour that she beseeched her own parents, Uranus and Gaia, to help her save her latest child. Following their advice she journeyed to Crete where, in a deep cavern under the forests of Mount Aegeum, she gave birth to her son. Gaia took charge of the newly born baby, while Rhea wrapped a large stone in swaddling clothes and presented it to the unsuspecting Cronus, who promptly swallowed it. Later, when Zeus reached manhood, he sought the aid of Metis to free his imprisoned brothers and sisters, whereupon Metis administered a draught to the old god which caused him to vomit up the stone, together with Hestia, Demeter, Hera, Hades and Poseidon, after which Cronus retired to some unspecified place to dwell in bliss or, according to other authorities, plunged into mysterious slumber in Thule.[7]

Here we have a parable-like tale which confirms the Egyptian story of the acquisition of the five epagomenal days, while also explaining how time both builds and destroys successive generations of life on Earth and the cultures through which they express themselves.

Hermes was the other Greek deity associated with time, and like his Norse counterpart, Loki (the Teutonic Loge), he was something of a trickster. In the Norse/Teutonic version Loki was the chaotic element that continually wrought havoc among the gods, whereas the Greeks saw Hermes in a somewhat different light. To them Hermes was a god of communication and commerce, the messenger of the gods, and provided one was constantly alert to his subtleties he could be, like Time, a good servant. In alchemy, Time/Thoth/Mercury is the Mercurius, about which Jung commented liberally (see Chapter 9).

The Greeks also had three other female immortals who were associated with time. These were the Moerae or Fates. The first was Clotho, the Spinner, whose attribute was the spinning wheel or spindle which spun the thread of life itself. Clotho represented the future as fashioned in the present. Then came Lachesis, the Apportioner, who held a measuring stick or rod, which represented that element of good fortune to which each person was supposedly entitled. The final member of this trio of grey-haired goddesses was Atropos, the Inevitable, who was depicted holding an appropriate cutting implement, signifying that inescapable pattern of entropy that we call death.

Australia

The Australian aborigines see the answer to time's riddle as lying in their belief that events exist neither *before* nor *after*, but all at once. In the *Dreamtime*, all past, present and future coexist, and one of the main tribal initiations consists of helping the initiate to become aware of the eternal *nowhere*.[8]

India

The Hindu god, Siva, is seen by many scholars as the epitome of
Time. Like Time he destroys, but like Time he is also merciful.
Siva was *Natardja*, the king of dancing, the halo fringed with fire
surrounding him symbolizing the whole cosmos, while his various
other attributes represent the life-death cycle as played out at all
levels. In his dance *Tandava*, the god destroys and creates by
which, at the end of a cosmic period, the world of appearances
disappears but actually is reintegrated into the Absolute. Siva's
dance also symbolizes divine activity as the source of movement in
the universe, particularly in relation to the cosmic functions of
creation – conservation, destruction, incarnation and liberation.[9]

Tomas sees the three-faced Trimurti of Brahma, Vishnu and
Siva as having been invented by the sages of ancient India to
symbolize the cycle of time. He tells us: 'Brahma created the
visible world in the past, Vishnu preserves it in the present, and
Siva will destroy creation in the future to build new worlds out of
the debris of the old. Death appears at the feast of life but life is
always born at the funeral of worlds.[10]

The passage of time as related to evolution on Earth was also
understood by the ancient peoples of the Indian subcontinent. The
Sanskrit *Book of Manu* (*c.* second century BC) describes the
evolutionary progression from bacteria and microorganisms via
plant, insect, fish, reptile, mammal and anthropoid life forms.
Likewise, the *Incarnations of Vishnu* are listed in the following
order: fish, tortoise, boar, lion-man, dwarf, man with axe, Rama
and Krishna.[11] A deeper study of the symbology described in
these different manifestations of some obscure but meaningful
divine principle might prove rewarding to the student. I have my
own ideas about them, and although several of them are anthropo-
logically recognizable there are the misfits, if you care to think
about it. Strangely enough, the ancient Irish legends tell a very
similar story, especially in *The Book of the Dun Cow*, which is
'related' by one man who, upon death, assumed the bodies of a
series of creatures in this order: a stag, a boar, an eagle and a
salmon, each of which contributed its own chapter of the tale.

Gautama the Buddha is credited with several sayings concerning time, the best known probably being: 'I believe that the world
is going to exist forever and forever. It will never come to an end.
And anything that has no end, has no beginning. The world was
not created by anyone. The world always was.' In defining the
present, he commented: 'Just as a chariot wheel rolls only at one
point of the tyre, and in resting rests only at one point, in the same

way, the life of a living being lasts only for a period of one thought.' In respect of the latter statement, author Andrew Tomas added: 'But Time as a whole is the wheel.'[12]

The study of time also features in many other ancient cultures. The Chinese, Incas, Copan and Palenque Mayas, and other ancient peoples of Central and South America, each had their own methods of recording and acknowledging time's arrows. Time even crept into the realm of simple superstition in the form of a herb which must, at some point in the distant past, have derived its name from some ancient source – thyme. According to old folklore, the souls of the dead were once thought to dwell in the flowers of thyme (timelessness – a folk memory of some more profound metaphysical knowledge, perhaps?) as they also did in bean-blossoms and foxgloves.

The latter two associations can be traced back to ancient Egyptian belief concerning what Paracelsus later incorporated in his famous *Doctrine of Signatures*, but since it is time that interests us at present let us see what else we can glean from this strange superstition and play on words. It seems that the scent of thyme has always been associated with psychic manifestations of those who have passed on. In certain parts of Britain it was the custom to bring thyme and southernwood into the house after a death and keep them there until the corpse was taken out for burial. However, thyme was always omitted from the coffin dressing for 'the dead have nothing to do with time'.[13] This curious punning superstition is also found in many other countries. Notwithstanding its association with death, thyme was also associated with the gift of courage and was included in folk-remedies as a cure for depression (time cures all?).

Scientific Knowledge Among the Ancients

The so-called Emerald Tables of Hermes have proved of interest to students of ancient science and esoterica alike. Believed by mystics to have been bequeathed to the priests of ancient Egypt by Thoth himself, known to the Greeks as Hermes, they constitute one of the oldest alchemical texts. The original tablets were allegedly found by Alexander the Great in the tomb of Hermes who, according to the legend, had their fifteen cryptic sentences engraved on an emerald plate with a diamond stylus. A text eventually surfaced in an Arabic copy in the care of the eighth-century Arab scholar and alchemist Jabir (Geber), still considered by some as the father of science, although how much of it was altered during the Dark Ages we may never know. For many years the content of these tables was viewed as nothing more than a product of the Middle Ages, until research carried out by the eighteenth-century scholar, Dr Sigismund Bacstrom, traced them to c. 2500 BC. Several of the statements contained within these texts carry scientific and cosmological connotations that are relevant to both time and modern physics.

The opening sentence, for example, runs thus: *What is above is like what is below, and what is below is like what is above to effect the wonders of one and the same work*. The microcosmic/macrocosmic allusion here is obvious, while this simple statement can also be read at the level of quantum physics and honeycomb universes. In another passage we have:

> All things owe their existence to the Only One, so all things owe their origins to the One Only Thing.
> Separate the earth from the fire, the subtile from the gross, carefully and skilfully. This substance ascends from the earth to the sky, and descends again on the earth – and thus the superior and inferior are increased in power.
> This is the potent power of all forces for it will overcome all that is fine and penetrate all that is coarse because in this manner was the world created.[14]

Minute particles moving at incalculable speeds, interpenetrating denser particles – the ancients seemed well aware of these facts, content to comprehend their principles without the need of physical confirmation. We, in contrast, struggle with our particle accelerators and the ever-expanding range of technological impediments to reproduce measurable manifestations of the materially immeasurable.

Common among most mythologies is the theme of a vanished Golden Age that existed prior to the Flood, when mankind had access to knowledge so dangerous that the gods found it necessary to destroy the whole race. In the Maya *Popol Vuh*, for example, it is said that the ' "First Men" could see what was far and what was very small, and they surveyed the four quarters of the globe. The Gods closed the eyes of the first men, and all their knowledge was lost.'[15] The allusion here to a knowledge of the worlds of quantum and superspace is blatantly obvious.

However, mythology was by no means the only way chosen by the sages of old to convey a deeper knowledge of the true nature of the universe. Democritus of Abdera (460–370 BC), the Greek philosopher and scientist, postulated that the universe was made up of minute particles, or atoms, multifariously arranged to account for the differing properties of matter. The physicist

Heisenberg (of Uncertainty Principle fame), wrote a treatise on the debate between Plato and Democritus, which included the subheadings, 'The concept of Matter in Ancient Philosophy'. 'The Answer of Modern Science to the Old Problems', and 'The Consequences for the Evolution of Human Thought in Our Own Day'. These are produced in full on pages 45–54 in *Quantum Questions*.

According to Andrew Tomas, Democritus received his information from Moschus the Phoenician, although Moschus' knowledge is nearer the truth because he emphasized the divisibility of the atom. The Greek philosophers were apparently impressed by the information contained in the Emerald Tables of Hermes, since they also claimed that there was no distinction between the other stellar bodies and the Earth.

Leucippus (fifth-century BC) and Epicurus (341–270 BC) also favoured the atomic theory, while the Roman scholar Lucretius (first century BC) wrote of atoms 'rushing everlastingly throughout all space' and undergoing 'myriad changes under the disturbing impact of collisions'.[16] In his *Nature of the Universe*, Lucretius stated '. . .there can be no centre in infinity'[17] which is seen by some as representing a cornerstone of Einstein's Theory of Relativity.

In his books *We Are Not The First* and *Beyond the Time Barrier*, Tomas gives us several other examples of pre-knowledge:

* Pythagoras' belief in the spherical nature of the Earth, which knowledge he taught in his school at Crotona (c. 580–500 BC).
* Aristarchus of Samos' theory that the Earth revolved around the sun (c. 270 BC).
* Heraclitus' statement, 'The way up and the way down are one and the same . . . one and the same creature is alive and dead, awake and asleep, young and old' (fifth century BC).
* Zeno of Elea, who in the fifth century BC demonstrated the relativity of motion and time with the question: 'If the flying arrow is at every instant of its flight at rest in a space equal to its length, when does it move?'
* Philolaus predicted the existence of antimatter (also in the fifth century BC) in his notion that an invisible body he called 'antichthon' or 'antiearth' existed in our solar system. Working on the assumption that the law of antimatter as applied to minute particles also applies to larger bodies, Philolaus might yet prove to be correct.
* Anaximenes upset Alexander the Great with the statement that he had conquered but one Earth, there being many, many others in infinite space (c. 570–500 BC).
* Anaxagoras (c. 500–428 BC) also taught that there were 'other earths' in the universe.

* Plato, (c. 428–347 BC) writing in the *Statesman* mentioned an oscillating universe periodically reversing its time-arrow and sometimes moving from the future into the past. Bearing in mind the information given in preceding chapters, it would seem that he was very much on the mark.
* Apollonius of Tyana, the Greek Neo-Pythagorean philosopher who was contemporary with Christ, in a letter to Consul Valerius, wrote: 'There is no death of anyone but only in appearance even as there is no birth of anyone save only in seeming. The change from being to becoming seems to be birth, but in reality no one is ever born nor does one ever die. It is simply a being visible and then invisible: the former through the density of matter, and the latter because of the subtlety of being – being which is ever the same, its only change being motion and rest.
* Nicolaus, Cardinal of Cusa, a fifteenth-century scholar, also conceived of a universe without a centre.
* Giordano Bruno, a Dominican monk who was burned at the stake as a heretic for his scientific and neo-paganistic beliefs, stated in one of his books that there are an infinite number of suns in the universe, many of which have planets revolving around them in the same way that our own Earth revolves around the sun. He also expressed the opinion that some of these worlds were populated.
* Lao Tse (sixth–fifth century BC) who founded Taoism, taught that everything in the universe is created according to a natural law, or *Tao*, which operates throughout the whole of the cosmos. All creation is the result of the interplay between two basic cosmic principles – the male *Yang* and the feminine *Yin*. (Positive and negative charges in the nuclear world determine nature's myriad manifestations.)
* The atomic structure of matter receives emphasis in the Brahmin treatises *Vaisesika* and *Nyaya*, while the *Yoga Vasishta* states: There are vast worlds within the hollows of each atom, multifarious as the specks in a sunbeam.

There are many, many other examples that could be cited. The question is, however, how did these people know of such matters long before there was the technology available to prove them? You, the reader may have your theories, the physicists will have theirs, but I have mine and here it is.

There was, in the archaic past, a civilization that did possess all the knowledge we have, as the ancient myths have suggested, and much more. But its development was way ahead of that of the rest of humanity at the time, so when it met its ultimate fate in a major axis tilt, those who did escape with their lives found themselves in highly primitive surroundings which afforded them no materials or technology to perpetuate their extensive knowledge. The ancient tales of their achievements were therefore relegated to the realms of magic and superstition – the fairy-tales and myths of archaism – to which serious students of the human mind, such as the great psychiatrist Carl Gustav Jung, have only recently started to accord some relevance. Greater minds than mine have made this observation, physicist and Nobel prizewinner Professor Frederick Soddy, for example, who also viewed these ancient records as something other than fable. In the *Interpretation of Radium* (1909), Soddy wrote:

> Can we not read into them some justification for the belief that some former forgotten race of men attained not only to the knowledge we have so recently won, but also to the power that is not yet ours?[18]

Of course, when Soddy wrote those words nuclear power was as yet undiscovered, although some great minds, like Soddy's, doubtless retained a far memory of it in their deep unconscious. I am also convinced that memories of those past achievements are recorded in what Jung would refer to as the 'collective unconscious', and what metaphysicians might view as memories of former lives, which I like to think of as the experiences of psyche-fragments in other time-zones or universes: past, present and future, but more of this later.

While on the subject of Nobel prizewinners, in 1978 I was privileged to be taken to lunch by a scientist who had received this acknowledgement for his work some years earlier. During the course of the meal he confided to me that he had clear memories from his youth of being a sonics scientist in Atlantis, which he referred to affectionately as the 'Old Country', the recollection of which brought tears to his eyes. I questioned him as to why he had not researched sonics in his present life and he replied that he had been warned subconsciously against pursuing this line of scientific enquiry as 'the world was not yet ready to handle that kind of power'. Strangely enough, although scientists as a body are often openly hostile to anything even vaguely approaching the paranormal, in private many of them share the same views as Professor Soddy and my own contact. In fact, I have engaged in deep discussions with some highly qualified men, 'On the condition that none of this is repeated publicly – one has one's career to think of, and all that.'

Many students of modern science who are also interested in the far past, have applied their talents to the study of ancient texts, both religious and secular, in the hope of discovering some firm link between myth and scientific reality. In the *Vision of Isaiah*, for example, the Old Testament prophet is taken to heaven by an angel and enjoys a stay of two weeks among the heavenly hosts. On his return, however, he is shocked to discover that thirty-two years have passed on Earth while he has been away. Time dilation? Some might think so, but the gap between logical supposition and empirical fact is still far too wide for most scientists to bridge, even if, in some quiet moment, their right-brain intuition might prompt them to consider it.

Our examination of time in myth, history and religion has so far been limited to the pre-Christian faiths, whose scholars appear to have been far more open to reason and enquiry when it came to the nature of the universe than their Christian equivalents. St Augustine, however, was a possible exception, a fact which the famous astronomer, mathematician and physicist, Sir James Jeans (1877–1946), saw fit to comment upon in his statement:

> Modern scientific theory compels us to think of the creator as working outside time and space – which are part of his creation – just as the artist is outside his canvas. It accords with the conjecture of Augustine: '*Non in tempore, sed cum tempore, finxit Deus mundum*'. Indeed the doctrine dates back as far as Plato: '*Time and the heavens came into being at the same instant in order that, if they were ever to dissolve, they might be dissolved together. Such was the mind and thought of God in the creation of time.*'[19]

On another occasion Augustine wrote: 'Time is like a river made up of events which happen, and its current is strong; no sooner does anything appear than it is swept away.'

The early Christian Gnostics appeared to be as curious about the phenomenon of time as the contributors to those Greek, Egyptian and Oriental sources from which they culled much of their knowledge. Towards the end of the nineteenth century, the Theosophical scholar, G. R. S. Mead, assembled a series of tractates and fragments from Hellenistic Theosophy and the Gnosis, which included extracts and the extant sermons of several early philosophers, scholars, historians and Church fathers, which he translated from Greek, and the versions of earlier Egyptian and Hebrew texts. This compilation was entitled *Thrice Greatest Hermes*. In view of the numerous translations and retranslations to which these texts have obviously been subjected, the reader is cautioned to allow for the inevitable errors in interpretation that must have crept in as the scholars of one age tackled the ideas and theories of a much earlier generation. Mead's *Hermes Trismegistus* comes in three volumes, and it is in the first part of Volume 3, entitled the *Stobaeus*, that the following excerpt concerning time is to be found:

1. Now to find out concerning the three times; for they are neither by themselves, nor [yet] are they at-oned; and [yet] again they are at-oned, and by themselves [as well].

   For should'st thou think the present is without the past, it can't be present unless it has become already past. [1]

   For from the past the present comes, and from the present future goes.

   But if we have to scrutinize more closely, thus let us argue:
2. Past time doth pass into no longer being this, [1] and future [time] doth not exist, in its not being present; nay, present even is not present, in its continuing.

   Time, then, which *stands* not [steady] (ἔστηκε), but which is on the turn, without a central point at which to stop, – how can it be labelled *in-stant* (ἐνεστώζ), [2] seeing even that it hath no power to *stand* (ἐστάναι)?

   Again, past joining present, and present [joining] future, they [thus] are one; for they are not without them [3] in their sameness, and their oneness, and their continuity.

   Thus [then], time's both continuous and discontinuous, though one and the same [time].

[1] That is, apparently, 'present'.
[2] The usual term in Greek for 'present', but I have here translated it by 'instant' in order to keep the word-play, which would otherwise entirely vanish in translation.
[3] That is, apparently, any one without the other two, or any two without the other one. [20]

I have included the author's notes for the benefit of any Greek scholars among my readers who might see fit to question Mead's interpretation.

The archaic turn of phrase notwithstanding, it appears from the aforegoing that both the arrow of time, and time as taken in the relativity context are being discussed here, and one can only regret the later omission of such knowledge in those teachings that were to influence the civilized world for the ensuing centuries. One cannot help wondering what other gems of scientific knowledge and ancient wisdom have been denied to us as a result of the destruction of the great libraries of the past. Here are a few examples to start with, there are doubtless many, many more: the Papyri of the library of the Temple of Ptah in Memphis were totally destroyed; the collection of Pisistratus in Athens (sixth century BC) was ravaged; the library of Pergamus in Asia Minor, which contained some 200,000 volumes, shared a similar fate; the Carthaginian library with its half-a-million volumes was razed by the Romans in 146 BC; and the greatest tragedy of all, the burning of the Alexandrian library in Julius Caesar's Egyptian campaign, during which some 700,000 priceless scrolls – 400,000 in the Bruchion and 300,000 in the Serapeum – were lost. An imaginative versifier named Lucian asserted that the glow of the conflagration could be seen as far as Rome. Following this devastation, the Bruchion was rebuilt and what was left of the old library of Pergamus was moved to the new building, which the city had bequeathed to the Senate, and which the infatuated Mark Anthony handed over to Cleopatra, last of the Ptolemies.

With the decline of Alexandria, its libraries shared a similar fate; Julian the Emperor (AD 360–63) helped himself to a goodly portion. The Christian fanatics stormed the Serapeum in 387, razing the temple to its foundation and leaving only empty shelves in the once famous library. The final insult to learning occurred in 641 when Amru, general of Omar, second in succession to the Prophet, fed the furnaces of the 4000 baths of Alexandria for full six months with the Bruchion's priceless treasures.[21] Those interested in the Trismegistic literature or the other translations effected by Mead are referred to the Bibliography, or to my book *Ancient Egypt: The Sirius Connection*.

Endnotes

1. A. Tomas, *Beyond the Time Barrier,* p. 43.
2. Larousse *Encyclopedia of Mythology,* p. 56.
3. *Ibid.* p. 56.
4. E. A. Wallis Budge, *The Gods of the Egyptians*, Vol. I, p. 401.
5. *Ibid.* p. 405.
6. J. Goodman, *The Earthquake Generation*, pp. 160–1.
7. Larousse, *op. cit.* p. 96.
8. Tomas, *op. cit.* p. 43.
9. Larousse, *op. cit.* p. 386.
10. Tomas, *op. cit.* p. 34.
11. Tomas, *We Are Not The First*, pp. 98–9.
12. A. Tomas, *Beyond the Time Barrier*, p. 24 and p. 42.
13. E. Radford, *Encyclopedia of Superstitions*, edited and revised by Christina Hole, p. 340.
14. A. Tomas, *We Are Not The First*, pp. 71–2.
15. R. Mooney, *Gods of Air and Darkness*, p. 47.
16. A. Tomas, *We Are Not the First*, p. 72.
17. *Ibid.* p. 73.

18. *Ibid.* p. 74.
19. *Quantum Questions*, edited by K. Wilber, p. 143.
20. G. R. S. Mead, *Thrice Greatest Hermes* Vol. 3, pp. 28–9.
21. G. R. S. Mead, *Fragments of a Faith Forgotten*, pp. 105–6.

7
The Psychology of Time

*I have been convinced that at least a part of our psychic existence is
characterized by a relativity of space and time. This relativity seems to
increase, in proportion to the distance from consciousness, to an absolute
condition of timelessness and spacelessness.*

C. G. JUNG[1]

There would appear to be little doubt that, as far as the human
psychology is concerned, time functions differently for each
individual, and our perception of time is altered, or coloured, by
the train of events that occupy our lives. Thus, from a psychological standpoint, it could be said that we do not all perceive
the passage of time identically; personality types and individual
responses to given situations are among the deciding factors as to
how time affects us.

Time and Human Consciousness

How many of us can recall with any degree of accuracy events that
took place even as recently as ten years ago? One retains the
overall picture, but individual experiences tend to become lost
somewhere in the memory banks of that complex computer we
call the brain. Of course, they are not really lost, but life's
circumstances, and our inclination to rely more on our left-brain
hemisphere than our right, have predisposed us to forget what our
subconscious minds have relegated to the realms of trivia, or
chosen to file away in some dark corner of the subconscious for
traumatic reasons. It has been speculated by some researchers that
the main human memory circuits are locked away in the deep
unconscious, a view I tend to endorse. These 'far memories',
together with those traumas associated with our existence in the
band of time we relate to our present 'reality' may, however, be

122

accessed by a skilful psychologist or hypnotherapist, who is able to probe the appropriate depths via the right-brain exit to Outer Time.

Memory also has the facility of allowing us to forget the unpleasant aspects of our past, favouring instead that rosy-hued mindscape we call nostalgia. How many of us, for example, are able to recall the agonies of excruciating pain? Only when some extreme trauma has been experienced are the marks of intense physical (or mental) suffering etched so deeply on our psyches that we relive them time and time again when reminded by some untimely phrase or incident, or by the content of some news report or documentary programme, or perhaps in sleep state. Fortunately, for most of us, the defence mechanisms of the brain click into action and the agony of a ruptured appendix or road accident are soon forgotten. Perhaps the deciding factor as to how we react to the emergencies we encounter during our sojourn through this particular band of time is their imprint on our psyche more than the scars they leave on our bodies.

Nostalgia reminds us of those questionably happy days in the past when all was *seen to be* well. We may recall with warmth the comradeship of our wartime colleagues – what a super bunch of chaps (or girls) they were! Were we to be more honest with ourselves, we would also remember the hardships and inconveniences we endured, and how we couldn't stand a certain non-commissioned officer who gave us a really rough ride at the time. Likewise, time's effect on the minds of parents whose children are grown up and flown the coop is also easily observable. Forgotten are the difficulties, tears and anguish of child-rearing experiences; only the rosy memories, many of which are pure delusions, remain. A similar response has been observed in couples who have spent years bickering, and who delight in informing their neighbours, relatives and friends how glad they will be to see the back of each other. Come the fall of Cronus' scythe and we have a different story, however, the deceased partner assuming an almost deified place in their memory. It is a fact that time can both distort our sense of reality and play some strange tricks with the human emotions.

Certain psychological types are more prone to fall victims to time's foibles than others, notably paranoics, depressives, cyclothymes and obsessives. The tendency to escape into what Jung refers to as 'no time' during periods of stress or depression is something of which we are all guilty. In fact, this is surely one of time's 'safe harbours' to which we may all retreat when the conditions of the present prove too hard to face. People under the influence of certain drugs have also experienced a sense of time slowing down for them. From these and other observations, we may observe that time's energies are neither good nor evil, but like all other forms of natural cosmic energy they are neutral until coloured by the minds of those who employ them, albeit unconsciously.

Brain, Mind and Psyche

When we are enjoying ourselves time seems to fly but during those dark days when everything seems to go awry, or we are afflicted by boredom, it gives the impression of dragging. But why should this be, for surely the time on our clocks remains whatever our mood? Are these illusions therefore created by our brains, minds, psyches? Let us first of all establish the role played by (a) the brain, (b) the mind, and (c) the psyche or transpersonal self, in the absorption and negotiation of time's energies. This takes us into the world of such psychological complexities as behaviour, the nature of consciousness, the free-will premise, dreams and parallel universes, and many more highly debatable issues about which most of us tend to take one side or other. For example, can our thinking mechanisms be reduced solely to mechanical functions within the brain? There are three schools of thought on this subject:

> MONOISM which views the mind as purely the expression of the physical brain, the size, nature and internal workings of that organ being the deciding factor as to what sort of mentality the individual may possess.
> DUALISM which is concerned with some external and, to date, immeasurable energy field that exerts a programming influence over the physical brain.
> METAPHYSICAL BELIEF which conceives of the brain as purely the material tool of the psyche, spirit, or 'essence'.

The fact that the brain can be altered surgically and the mind still remain strong leaves (a) open to question, while (b) could simply be a more scientific way of describing (c) without involving ethical or religious bias. Paul Davies comments:

> From the viewpoint of neurophysiology, the brain can be studied at two levels. The lower level concerns the workings of individual neurones (brain cells) and their interconnections, establishing what makes them fire and how the electrical pulses propagate between

neurones. At a higher level, the brain can be regarded as a fantastically complex *network* around which electrical *patterns* meander. If, as seems clear, mental processes are associated with patterns of neural activity rather than the state of any particular neurone, then it is the latter approach that is most likely to illuminate the higher functions of behaviour and consciousness. [2]

Davies then proceeds to tell his readers how computer designers are anxious to discover how the brain performs certain integrative tasks so that they can think in terms of designing 'intelligent' machines.

There are certain points to be taken into consideration here. The first involves the premise that intelligence, as such, is still very much an unknown factor in that it is *not* synonymous with creativity. In fact, the creative processes, which are essentially right-brain orientated, are frequently incompatible with left-brain logic, as Einstein himself averred, and it is more than often the *creative* mind that is responsible for those discoveries that have aided the growth of civilization, which the left-brain orientated technologists then go about the task of developing. Although a high intelligence quotient is usually taken as indicative of intellectual ability, some people I have known personally who have passed the Mensa tests with flying colours have been anything but original thinkers, their sole skills lying in their ability to develop or expound upon the ingenuities of other, more creative minds with, perhaps, lower IQs.

The second issue concerns programming. A computer cannot function without a program. Alone it is simply a conglomeration of metal, plastic, and microchips, but add the correct program and it sails into action. Assuming the absence of the psyche, or some other external agency with programming capabilities, who designs our programs? From a sociological viewpoint this could be seen to land us neatly on the slippery doorstep of the nature versus nurture controversy. Taken in the overall picture, however, both of these are, in fact, in the employ of time in that they constitute deciding factors when it comes to our utilization of time's energies as we pass through them.

Which leads us to our next consideration: the nature of consciousness, a blanket term used to designate mind, intelligence, reason, awareness, free will, alertness, and so forth. In the time context, consciousness, as equated with mind, is viewed as separate from physiological cerebral functioning and regarded more as an expression of the psyche, 'essence', or transpersonal Self, which, in turn, relays its Outer Time instructions to the brain via its right hemisphere. So, although the term 'mind' would appear to mean different things to different people, according to which school of psychology, humanism, metaphysics or religion they may adhere to, there is no doubt that 'mind' as such, no matter what its true nature or function might be, is a force in itself that motivates and influences the growth and behaviour of matter and is, as such, an agent of time. This influence may apply negatively (as with psychosomatic illness), or through any beneficial mental discipline according to the inclinations and strength of character of the individual.

Time and Synchronicity

Jung was of the opinion that scientific thinking was unreasonably dominated by notions of causality for the explanation of physical events. The probability factor in quantum mechanics, therefore, impressed him because of its tendency to undermine strict causality, and from this he derived the idea that there may exist, alongside causality, another physical principle that could connect events that might otherwise be observed as functioning independently. 'Events in general are related to one another on the one hand as causal chains, and on the other by a kind of *meaningful cross-connection*.'[3] To this physical principle Jung gave the name 'synchronicity'. He assembled a considerable amount of anecdotal evidence for his synchronicity principle, of the kind to which most of us can easily relate, such as running into an old friend one has not seen in years shortly after talking about him, or misdialling a telephone number to discover that the person on the other end of the line has something for which you have been searching for a long time.

Two examples of this spring to mind. The first concerns a college friend of mine who had been a pupil at a major public school for girls. Prior to setting forth to sing solo in a classical music concert she remarked to me how she had often wondered what happened to a rather way-out classmate whom she had not seen for some twenty years. While driving to her destination she was held up in a three-lane traffic jam. The woman in the car beside her looked somehow familiar and, sure enough, it proved to be the very classmate she had mentioned to me that morning. Needless to say, they agreed to stop at the next service station to exchange information.

The second 'coincidence' occurred when I was in need of a particular book for research purposes. While travelling to my destination on a London Underground train I was joined by a group of noisy students who were celebrating the fact that they had just obtained their medical degrees. One young lady was carrying a bag containing several books and her male companion remarked: 'You won't need those any more, love, sling them out, right now!' Whereupon the girl in question dumped three weighty volumes in my lap with nothing more than a 'Have a nice day!' At which point the doors opened to the next station and they all disappeared singing and carousing wildly. Needless to say, my present proved to be exactly the books I needed at the time.

Although Jung reinforced his synchronicity idea with countless examples from his many case histories, and his ideas were espoused and followed up by Arthur Koestler in his book *The Roots of Coincidence*, few scientists really took him seriously which was, and still is, a great pity, since his research was highly scientific and impeccable. But then that is likely to be the case when one discipline is dealing with the purely mechanical, and the other with the human mind which, in spite of its mechanistic-type neural functioning, seldom responds to the precise laws of causality. Regarding the bounds of coincidence Jung wrote:

> All natural phenomena of this kind are unique and exceedingly curious combinations of chance, held together by the common meaning of their parts to form an unmistakable whole. Although meaningful coincidences are infinitely varied in their phenomenology, as acausal events they nevertheless form an element that is part of the scientific picture of the world. Causality is the way we explain the link between two successive events. Synchronicity designates the parallelism of time and meaning between psychic and psychophysical events, which scientific knowledge has so far been unable to reduce to a common principle. [4]

Paul Davies, however, admits that quantum mechanics permits the existence of correlations between simultaneous events separated in space which would be impossible in any traditional scientific conception of reality, and has conceived of a way in which the synchronicity principle could be accommodated by particle physics without crossing the scientific-metaphysical ring-pass-not. The latter concept and explanatory diagram is uniquely his. Those interested are referred to *The Cosmic Blueprint* for full details.

As I see it, there are several explanations: (1) time as we know it is only one of many 'bands'. At times these may touch temporarily or converge for a period of microseconds only, but this is sufficient for the supersensitive neurones of the brain to pick up and translate. Let us say that two time-zones, each carrying a specific program, converge on a given point. One person is involved with one program and another is busy working through the second. The paths of both therefore cross at the point of convergence so that any features shared between the specific programs will be registered automatically, albeit subconsciously, by the persons concerned, as in the incident of my 'book' anecdote. This concept could, I am sure, be easily explained in quantum terms. (2) Since, at a given frequency in the universe, all time is one, and all sentient beings may well be endowed with an innate capacity to negotiate both Inner and Outer Time *simultaneously*, unconsciously if not consciously, then those cosmic laws that designate the evolutionary processes within both the individual and the world at large will be seen to come into play. In other words, when the time is *right*, events deemed essential for our progress, or the world's as the case may be, will take place in the natural course of events. Remember, the apparently chaotic behaviour of minute particles at close quarters may be seen to give way to symmetries of great beauty and singular purpose when viewed from afar, as may be shown in the study of fractals (see Glossary). The combination of Computer Science and Chaos Science, has, of late, contributed generously to our knowledge of cosmic principles at work at different frequencies, fractals in particular, helping us to give form to the abstract.

The interplay between the space-time continuum and synchronicity and the human psyche is also highlighted by Jung in his statement:

> I defined synchronicity as a psychically conditioned relativity of space and time. Rhine's experiments show that in relation to the psyche space and time are, so to speak, 'elastic' and can apparently be reduced almost to vanishing point, as though they were dependent on psychic conditions and did not exist in themselves but were only 'postulated' by the conscious mind. In man's original view of the world, as we find it among primitives, space and time have a very precarious existence. They become 'fixed' concepts only in the course of his mental development, thanks largely to the introduction of measurement.[5]

Time and the Sleep State

The fact that time assumes a different value during the sleep state has been shown in countless experiments. I have been aware of this conscious-unconscious change in time perception since early childhood but until my twenties I had nothing concrete upon which to establish its factual validity. Then one small, seemingly insignificant event occurred. I had an old alarm clock that had the irritating habit of making a loud click about three seconds before ringing. Time and time again I would hear this click and dive under the bedclothes to avoid the sharp ring that followed. One morning I heard the click and promptly fell asleep again. During those three seconds I underwent a dream sequence that would have taken several hours to enact in the so-called 'real' world. Then the alarm sounded, and I realized what had happened. Having studied dreams over a period of many years, both my own and those of others, I arrived at the conclusion that while we are asleep our brains disengage from Inner Time, thus allowing our psyches free range in timelessness. It was also in my study of dreams that I became convinced of the existence of parallel universes, and that we all engage in simultaneous multiple exist-ences during those times when our left brain hands over to its right hemisphere which, in turn, makes timelessness accessible via the psyche.

A question I am frequently asked regarding dreams is why some people are able to recall their night-time 'experiences' and others are not. This is, of course, tied up with the personality-type and individual psychology on the one hand, and what the metaphysi-cian would conceive of as the stage of *spiritual* maturity, on the other. I appreciate that my readers may well fall into two categories: those who will immediately dismiss the latter premise and scan the pages ahead to see if I get back to normality fairly soon, in which case the rest of the book might be worth reading, and those who either tentatively (or avidly) subscribe to the idea that our psyches enjoy an existence independent of the bodies we are occupying in the reality of the present. I hope to show that I am not alone in many of these ideas and that there is, in fact, plenty of hard-core scientific evidence to support them. However, since most of this will be dealt with in Chapter 8, let us return to the realms of sleep, and the adventures of the psyche in space-time while its body is resting and replenishing its energies.

In his latter days Jung wrote: 'Not only my own dreams, but also occasionally the dreams of others, helped to shape, revise, or confirm my views of a life after death.' Jung was also of the opinion that a complete picture of the world required the addition of another dimension,

... only then could the totality of phenomena be given a unified explanation. Hence it is that the rationalists insist to this day that parapsychological experiences do not really exist; for their world-view stands or falls by this question. If such phenomena occur at all, the rationalistic picture of the universe is invalid, because incomplete.[6]

Whether we care to admit it or not, during sleep the mind, brain, psyche, spirit, or whatever each authority may care to label that subtle essence that sparks our very existence, moves into a timeless, spaceless state that permits access to both the past and future. Some psychologists are of the opinion that dreams pre-programme or prepare us for forthcoming traumatic events that might otherwise affect adversely our mental health or stability. I recall hearing a radio programme in which this very subject was being discussed by a scientist and a psychologist, and one particular anecdote caught my attention. The scientist had apparently experienced a dream in which his father, who was also a man of science, and employed on a research programme in Australia, had suddenly died of a severe heart attack. Upon waking, his normal logic was temporarily suspended and he rang his father to see if he was, in fact, all right. In answering the call, the father, who had been schooled in the old Helmholtz tradition, instead of showing some appreciation for his son's concern, admonished him for being 'stupidly superstitious'. Greatly chastened, the son resumed his normal logic, but the shock he had experienced in the dream stayed with him for sometime afterwards, as though the event had really taken place. A few months later his father returned to England and the two were reunited. However, the older man had only been back a few weeks when he suffered a severe heart attack, from which he never recovered. The room in which this occurred was identical to the room the son had seen in his dream. When the sad event actually took place in the 'real' world, the son's sense of shock was considerably diminished, his own psyche having already prepared him subconsciously for the event during *sleep state*.

Telepathy

Totally relevant to our study of time is the faculty of telepathy, since it appears to cancel out both time and space, its messages superseding the speed of light. During my early metaphysical studies one of the first things I was taught was that thoughts were 'things', meaning that every thought carries an energy quotient and as such is capable of transference from one time-zone to another. It occurs to me that thoughts might well have a place in the quantum worlds, since they are for the most part abstract and without direction. In other words, assuming them to be particles of some kind, there will be times when they are 'fuzzy' (indistinct or fluctuating) and others when they are 'discrete' or distinct, the latter also implying a specific direction. The trained mind would therefore tend to produce more discrete particles than its undisciplined counterpart, which could account for the fact that some people are able to effect a mental control over their health and physical bodies (or physical phenomena generally), while others who embark on such popular practices as self-healing or visualization meet with little if any success.

Most people allow their thoughts to wander unguarded through time and space, and as such prove easy targets for telepaths or, as some would call them, 'psychics'. However, I am convinced that much that passes for psychism is telepathy pure and simple. In fact, I have watched it in action, especially in cases where the querent has a powerful, obsessional desire, which he or she strongly visualizes during the process of a reading. Unless thoughts of this kind are deliberately masked or concealed, any telepath worth his or her salt will have no problem in picking them up.

Parapsychologists working a research programme designed to either prove or disprove the existence of paranormal phenomena have encountered what is known as the 'experimenter effect'. In simple language this means that whoever is conducting the experiment is in some way able to affect its outcome. Observers noticed that when a test was set up by an ardent disbeliever, the results achieved were abnormally low, whereas the accuracy of the performance of the subjects increased dramatically under the direction of a scientist or researcher who wanted to believe. This could also be seen as confirmed in quantum paradoxes mentioned earlier, notably those of Schrödinger's Cat and Wigner's Friend, wherein the outcome of the experiment is inevitably decided by the action or observation of a person present.

So if, for example, you approach a psychic in the pious hope that he or she will pronounce your forthcoming date with a tall, dark man with a bushy moustache, or the luscious blonde from across the street, the odds are that you will get that precise feedback from your reader. But whether what you are told will necessarily come true will, of course, depend on the specific quality of your own thoughts. Are they, for example, the stuff that fantasy is made of or the more discrete particles that can provide a solid basis for the manifestation of the appropriate frequencies of time that will make that vision a reality? In plain language, it is all in the mind and some of us are stronger-minded than others!

Time and Prophecy

Prophecy has ever proved to be a fly in the ointment of rationalism, but since Einstein's equations allow for the movement of time forwards or backwards, why the problem? The answer, of course, lies in the fact that several branches of science still refuse to join Jung and his successors in the idea that human consciousness: (a) exists independently of the body; and (b) is capable of encompassing Outer Time, and that means *all* time, both backwards, forwards, up, down and sideways.

Edgar Cayce, the American seer, is usually cited as one of the best-known psychics of the twentieth century; his pronouncements are well documented by the foundation that still carries his name. Cayce is often referred to as the 'sleeping prophet' due to the fact that his prognostications were inevitably rendered while he was in a state of trance or 'asleep', a condition now referred to in parapsychology as an 'altered state of consciousness'. During such sessions, Cayce is reputed to have been able to diagnose any disease without any medical knowledge, and comment on events likely to take place on Earth in the years that lay ahead. The general consensus of opinion of those who investigated him during his life was that he had the ability to lock into some central memory bank which contained the records of both the past and future of this planet. As to the validity of his prophecies, although several are believed to have already come true, the main body of information he channelled concerned events destined to take place towards the end of this millennium. We wait with bated breath!

How we may or may not feel about the phenomenon of Edgar Cayce and similar seers of historical distinction, such as the fabled Nostradamus and Count Louis de Hamon (Cheiro), precognition, whether it be in sleep state or with full consciousness, does and has occurred both in everyday life and under test conditions. I myself have been involved in several of both kinds, one of which occurred when I was being interviewed by Leslie Smith for the Radio 4 programme 'Arrows of Time' (see Chapter 1). Some weeks prior to the actual transmission, I referred to a television programme which featured Dr Lyall Watson, in which he had made a certain statement. Unknown to me, the producers contacted Dr Watson, only to discover that the programme I had described, which included the given statement, was not scheduled to be shown for several weeks. At no other time and in no other programme had Dr Watson made any such statement. Smith asked him how he could account for my precognition (which, in all honesty, had not been given with prophecy, as such, in mind). I really believed I had seen the programme in question, but could not remember how or when. Perhaps I had dreamt it! Watson replied: 'If one is in this space–time, one can *remember* the future.'

That was but one well-documented and scientifically authenti-cated case of involuntary precognition. There are many, many others, some considerably more spectacular by far, including instances of voluntary use of the faculty, in which the seer cooperates with a researcher or experimenter by deliberately trying to probe the past or future in much the same way as the fortune-teller at the local fair. There is certainly plenty of evidence to support the theory that the human mind is capable of probing time, and although many books have been written on the subject, my favourite is *Explaining the Unexplained*, by the respected psychiatrist Professor Hans Eysenck, and Cambridge parapsycho-logist Dr Carl Sargent, who carried out their research under strict scientific conditions. Their verdict? Professor Eysenck reiterated his own words written a quarter of a century earlier:

> Unless there is a gigantic conspiracy involving some thirty University departments all over the world, and several hundred highly respected scientists in various fields, many of them originally sceptical to the claims of the psychical researchers, the only conclusion that the unbiased observer can come to must be that there does exist a small number of people who obtain knowledge existing either in other people's minds, or in the outer world, by means yet unknown to science.
>
> The only revision necessary now would be that the number of people involved is larger than it was then!
>
> To have a concern about fraud in science is reasonable. To try and 'explain' everything in terms of fraud is disreputable.
>
> Another historical factor which concerns some scientists is that parapsychology reeks of magic, long declared an enemy of science. Some scientists fear that the very attempt to set psi on a scientific basis will somehow encourage a superstitious, irrational, anti-scientific attitude. The perfect reply to this has been given by the astronomer Carl Sagan, attacking a repressive editorial in the (American) *Humanist* about astrology: 'The fundamental point is not that the origins of astrology are shrouded in superstition. This is true as well for chemistry, medicine and astronomy, to mention only three.'[7]

Eysenck and Sargent see that fanatical scepticism is as irrational as extreme gullibility. Both expose weaknesses and insecurities in the personalities of those concerned which are all too obvious to the trained observer. I recall taking part in a broadcast which featured a psychologist, a psychiatrist, and a brain surgeon whom I shall refer to as Professor X. The latter was as adamant on the question of telepathy and precognition as the great scientist Helmholtz, whose famous statement: 'Neither the testimony of all the Fellows in the Royal Society, nor even the evidence of my own senses, would lead me to believe in the transmission of thought from one person to another independent of the recognised channels of sense'[8] is often cited as a classic example of a closed mind. Professor X's reaction proved a source of some amusement to both the psychologist and psychiatrist, who spent the half-hour following the broadcast with me in the BBC canteen discussing the said gentleman's 'very obvious psychological hang-ups!' Were they prepared to concede that the mind might well function in Outer Time? They had certainly come across more incidents during the course of their researches than rational science could account for and they, too, like Eysenck and Sargent, viewed excessive rationality as part of the general 'fear' syndrome to which many so-called 'authorities' tend to fall victim when they feel their position may be threatened.

Time and Hypnosis

Regression under hypnosis has been used by psychiatrists and professional therapists working in the healing fields for many years now. The original idea was to take the client or patient back in time in order to discover at which point in their past the trauma occurred that was causing them mental distress in the present. Regression back to babyhood, or even earlier to the womb itself, was therefore not uncommon until it was discovered that consciousness actually existed prior to actual conception and even before then, albeit in some other form. Many hypnotherapists, psychiatrists or psychologists practising regression through hypnosis have tended to find their clients drifting back into former lives or 'reincarnations', which has been taken by many as evidence that people have lived lives on Earth before. The majority of the published works on this subject appear to deal exclusively with the human lives that people believe they have undergone in linear time. Other research, however, carried out by those less anxious to court the derision of the public at large and the scientific community in particular, have come up with some startlingly different results which intimate that some of us, anyway, have undergone experiences in life forms alien to our planet. Two examples that have come to my notice are (a) where the hypnotized person recalled being an elementary particle or helium atom involved in the continual atomic processes taking place on a distant star, and (b) in which the recall was of an incarnation in a highly advanced *feline* life form, centuries ahead of us both in terms of Earth time and overall evolutionary progress. This kind of pre-Earth experience was also revealed during experiments with hypnosis carried out in the Soviet Union.

I am by no means alone in my premise that all life forms throughout the universe house an intelligence, psyche, essence, call it what you will, and that that essence is capable of moving through both the time and space, and experiencing in life forms other than *Homo sapiens* throughout the cosmos. Metaphysical eyewash? Not really, since we are on the verge of discovering the subtle messages that minute particles can pass one to another through the space-time continuum, some of which carry such advanced information as the genetic and chemical construction of a whole species. If there is such a thing as an advanced Intelligence behind the formation of universes, and the evolutionary blueprint of a species such as *Homo sapiens*, the likelihood of that Essence taking on a human body at some point to obtain an inside view of how its handiwork was going is surely not beyond the bounds of logic.

This kind of thinking might well accord with Professor Fred Hoyle's panspermia theory, in which he postulates that the universe is a living, intelligent entity which scatters its interstellar particles (seeds?) by design, and in an orderly manner. Hoyle tells us:

> The concept of microorganisms distributed throughout interstellar space is not entirely new. It was considered already during the nineteenth century, in particular by British physicist Lord Kelvin. Unfortunately, however, the possibility of understanding biological evolution here on the Earth in terms of this concept was not appreciated, with the consequence that scientists became forced away from what is almost surely the correct theory by the rising tide of Darwinism. This was in spite of a valiant effort early in the present century by the Swedish chemist Svante Arrhenius to support the 'panspermia' theory, (meaning 'seeds everywhere'), by carefully reasoned arguments.[9]

Dr Rupert Sheldrake is another scientist who has embraced a similar notion of cosmic consciousness. Sheldrake has taken the morphogenetic field concept of developmental biology seriously, interpreting these phenomena as an entirely new type of physical effect. He has suggested that in some way the field stores the information about the final form of the embryo, and then proceeds to guide its development as it grows. Although some scientists, notably Gribbin, have seen this as a revival of old-fashioned teleology, Sheldrake introduces a new element in the form of 'morphic resonance', the idea being that once a new type of form has come into existence it sets up its own morphogenetic field. The know-how then spreads, and nature is able to guide by resonance the development of corresponding organisms.[10]

These morphogenetic fields are not, however, restricted to living organisms. Crystals possess them, Sheldrake tells us, and they are also closely connected with the faculty of memory. For example, once an animal has learned something new, others of the same species are able to follow suit. Sheldrake's 'fields' do not act in space and time in the normal causative fashion. In fact, their nature is something of an anathema to physicists generally and his work is not, therefore seen as part of the discoveries of mainstream science. Personally, I fail to see why crystals are not regarded as living organisms since they appear to exhibit an intelligence all of their own, but that is the subject of some future book. Teilhard de Chardin's philosophy of the conscious atom makes far more sense if we are to conceive of a great universal consciousness of which we are but minute particles. William Blake wrote: 'Everything exists, and not one sigh, nor smile, no tear, one hair, nor particle of dust, not one can pass away.'[11] In the light of my own researches and obervations over some forty years or more I find this concept far more acceptable.

But we must return to the question of hypnotic regression, or progression as the case may be, since the hypnotized mind is apparently capable of moving forward as much as backward in time. It has often been debated as to why a person should be able to recall details while under hypnosis that they are unable to bring to their conscious mind during ordinary recourse to memory. Gribbin remarks on the fact that the hypnotic trance state bears some similarity to sleep, and that the dreaming mind is less fixed in the time-circuits of earthly life than the conscious, waking mind. In fact, Gribbin raises a very cogent point in his question:

Is it possible that, under trance, rather than reliving past lives these subjects are somehow able to scan far across the time barrier to communicate with *other people* from the past? (Of course, we shouldn't forget that according to some philosophies, like that of Hoyle discussed elsewhere in this book, we may all be manifestations of one consciousness anyway!) With such a possibility in mind, we can relate such experiences more easily to those of dreams. Again, I see no objection to the idea that some minds may 'tune' more easily to a particular trance subject than others, so that the close identification of these regressions occurs only with a few scenes displaced 'out of time'.[12]

Dr Gribbin, I have arrived at exactly the same conclusion as you in this matter. I do not for one moment believe in the squadrons of Cleopatras, Queen Nefertitis, Jesus Christs, King Arthurs, and countless other characters from the linear historical past that appear to have descended upon us in this century. This kind of ego-tripping fantasy is guaranteed to evoke the derision of logical, thinking people. Jung's theory of the 'collective unconscious' is often blamed for much of what passes as the memories of former lives, while another school of thought sees all this information as being contained within those suspected time capsules – our genes, which we have already discussed in Chapter 4. The latter has, however, been dismissed by some authorities on the grounds that identical twins when regressed came up with different 'karmic' backgrounds. In other words, the pattern of their 'past lives' was quite different.

I do not believe for one moment that we have all of the answers to the hypnosis enigma, although, in keeping with other open-minded researchers, I think that some of the arguments put forward against the idea of former lives recalled while under hypnosis are facetious, to say the least. For example, the case of the young Welsh girl, who, during a visit to the dentist accidentally slipped into an hypnotic trance and spoke in archaic French. The dentist in question happened to have a tape recorder handy and the tape was later played back to some supposed 'experts'. Try as they could they were unable to find an incident in the girl's life in which she could have learned the French language in its ancient form until someone suddenly remembered that for two hours on *one* afternoon only, she had stood in for the usual cleaner at the home of a local clergyman of some learning, who just happened to have amongst the many books in his extensive library, a couple in archaic French. 'That is it,' the experts decided, 'she obviously browsed through these books at some point and her mind photographed the language.' Thereupon the puzzle was considered solved, and the learned gentlemen returned to their places of office in the comfortable knowledge that they had once again retrieved science from the mischievous web of superstition. (The girl, incidentally, denied touching any books.)

Two American psychologists have carried out extensive research in the area of past lives and hypnotic regression, with some interesting and enlightening results. Their books *You Have Been Here Before* (Dr Edith Fiore) and *Life Before Life* (Dr Helen Wambach) are well worth perusal in the light of many of the theories that have just been discussed. Specific EEG recordings appeared to relate to the subjective phenomena experienced in a particular brain-wave state. Wambach, for example, chose five cycles per second as the ideal state for receiving information on pre-birth experience.[13] No doubt this figure would vary in cases where the client is able to transcend the hominid experience and branch out into Outer Time proper. In other words, The Cosmos!

All the aforegoing examples and information simply reinforce the idea that during certain altered states of consciousness the mind is freed from the barriers of space and time, and able to enter worlds, dimensions or parallel universes in which time as we know it does not apply. I have had first-hand experiences of parallel universes in dream state, places to which I have never been, people I do not know or have never met in my normal conscious state, twists and turns in my life that have never occurred in the real world. I have also travelled along time's backward moving arrow; on one 'dream-occasion' I watched the pieces of dead and mutilated cat reassemble before my eyes to become the whole, live animal it was prior to its demise! (At this point it should be firmly stated that I have never, ever used or resorted to drugs of any kind to trigger my altered states of consciousness. I have been a teetotaller and vegetarian since my early twenties, and make a point of never eating late in the evening, so my 'dreams' cannot be blamed upon intakes of certain liquids or foodstuffs prior to retiring.) As a result I have concluded that many of the problems we experience in our day-to-day lives here in the present, are worked out in some parallel Earth in another universe. Hence the old saying: 'Sleep on it, and you'll know the answer in the morning.' And it seems to work.

Animals and Time

I am frequently asked whether animals, or insects for that matter, share a similar concept of time as ourselves. Obviously the limited lifespan of an insect, which may be only a matter of a few days, or

even hours, does not compare with the three-score and ten that we
are expected to live out, given the absence of illness, accident or
similar contingencies. But it has been postulated by experts that
for these creatures those few hours or days may constitute as full
an experience as our meagre seventy-five years or more. In other
words, the passage of time is relative and has a different meaning
for each species.

An area in which I do have some experience as far as animals
and time is concerned is in the world of felines. I have no doubt
whatsoever that a cat can experience timelessness during periods
of sleep. The REM's (rapid eye movements) normally associated
with dream activity may certainly be evidenced in cats. They are
also fully precognitive. For example, prior to the onset of a severe
winter, my cats have always grown extra thick coats and fattened
themselves up in preparation for the harsh days ahead. How do
they know? Call it instinct if you like, but I see no difference in
their precognitive abilities and those displayed by humans. They
also have a strong sense of time, and here is my evidence. Many
years ago an old wise-woman told me that if I ever had to go away
and leave my cats for any period, all I needed to do to reassure
them of my return was to tap them on the head for the number of
days and nights I would be absent. This I have always done. In
1978, when I left for Canada, I arranged for my cats to be flown
over on a specific date. I therefore gave them the requisite number
of taps from the day of my absence until the time we would be
reunited, and left them in the safe care of one of my dearest and
closest friends and her family.

However, some days after my arrival in Canada, when I
realized that things were not going to work out for me over there,
I telephoned my friend to cancel the date and hold fire. Up to that
point my three cats, two Siamese and a Burmese, had been
reasonably well and happy. But thereafter, they suddenly went
into decline and became highly disturbed. In fact, the eldest
Siamese became so ill that the vet pronounced her 'on the way
out', while the other two underwent severe withdrawal symp-
toms. My friend did not wish to worry me with this information,.
but another friend, who is also a writer and psychologist, felt I
should be told and made the transatlantic call. I packed my bags
and caught the first plane back, never again to return to Canada.

My friend's father met me at Heathrow and drove me back to
Cheltenham and there, waiting on the pavement outside my
friend's house, were my three cats, illness or no illness. Needless
to say, the old Siamese made a rapid and miraculous recovery and

lived to the ripe old age of twenty. For some strange and inexplicable reason, my head tapping had become the established signal between us for my period of absence, but they also *knew* the exact time of my return. My friend later confirmed that they each started to exhibit signs of excitement from the time I boarded the plane in Vancouver. Do animals have the ability to function in Outer Time? My verdict: of course, they do!

Endnotes

1. C. G. Jung, *Memories, Dreams and Reflections*, p. 283.
2. P. Davies, *The Cosmic Blueprint,* p. 183.
3. C. G. Jung, *The Structure and Dynamics of the Psyche*, p. 423.
4. *Ibid.* p. 530.
5. C. G. Jung, *Synchronicity*, p. 28.
6. C. G. Jung, *Memories, Dreams and Reflections*, pp. 282–83.
7. H. Eysenck, and C. Sargent, *Explaining the Unexplained*, p. 182.
8. *Ibid.* p. 184.
9. F. Hoyle, *The Intelligent Universe*, p. 158.
10. Davies, *op. cit.*, p. 164.
11. A. Tomas, *Beyond the Time Barrier*, p. 26.
12. J. Gribbin, *Timewarps*, p. 130.
13. H. Wambach, *Life Before Life*, p. 17.

8

The Metaphysics
of Time

*Today there is a wide measurement of agreement ... that the stream of
knowledge is heading towards a non-mechanical reality; the universe begins
to look more like a great thought than a great machine.*
SIR JAMES JEANS (1877–1946)

The reference to 'psi' in the previous chapter introduced briefly the
subject of parapsychology, which serves as an excellent springboard into the more abstract regions of metaphysics. Metaphysics
is the branch of philosophy that systematically investigates the
nature of first principles and problems of ultimate reality. It
includes the study of 'being' (ontology), and often the structure of
the universe (cosmology). While embracing critical philosophy in
general, it also emphasizes the subtle or abstract aspects of
speculative reasoning. The word 'metaphysics' derives from the
Greek *Ta meta ta phusika*, 'the (works) after the *Physics*', Aristotle's
treatise on transcendental philosophy, so called because it followed his works on physics.[1]

To the aforementioned definition I would like to add that today
metaphysics is very much concerned with creating a bridge
between science and philosophy, or physics and mysticism if you
prefer, since from the metaphysician's viewpoint each is basically
saying the same thing, but employing different semantics or terms
of reference. Metaphysics is not, as some might believe, another
name for the occult, magic or the various manifestations of psi,
nor is the metaphysician necessarily associated with any particular
religious, philosophical or transcendental school of belief or
enquiry. There may, of course, be those of metaphysical leanings
who have found solace in one of the major world religions,
Hermetic traditions, or schools of philosophy, but your author is
not among them.

The wide gap between science and the transcendental that has existed since chemistry separated from alchemy, astronomy from astrology, and medicine from natural healing, reached its peak in the first fifty years of the twentieth century. Now the gap is slowly but meaningfully closing, and if each side is prepared to jettison the less desirable aspects of its practices, a marriage between ancient and modern knowledge might well be part of our future heritage.

The popularity of recent books such as *The Tao of Physics* attests to the unprecedented interest in the relationship between modern quantum physics and mysticism that has arisen in the past decade. In fact, a book entitled *Quantum Questions*, edited by Ken Wilber, himself a scientist and author of *The Holographic Paradigm and Other Paradoxes*, refers to the mystical writings of some of the world's greatest physicists: Heisenberg, Schrödinger, Einstein, de Broglie, Jeans, Planck, Pauli and Eddington, all of whom, we are assured in the cover notes, 'express a deep belief that physics and mysticism are somehow fraternal twins'. Heisenberg in particular, aside from his work as a scientist, was both a mystic and metaphysician of the Pythagorean/Platonic school. But taking into account the branch of science in which they were engaged, why did all of these great physicists choose to embrace mysticism of one sort or another? Jung probably had the answer to this when he concluded that the human psyche accommodates an in-built, subliminal need to acknowledge the supramundane. Although the atheistically inclined may condemn this as irrational nonsense, experience bears out that even the most vehement unbelievers have been known to call upon some unseen power or hitherto denied force for help or comfort during times of extreme duress. There is also the compensatory angle, which any psychologist would be quick to point out. Too much emphasis on any one study or pursuit inevitably gives rise to a tendency to veer towards the opposite in one form or another in order to effect a sound, mental balance.

The 'Quantum Self' Theory

One of the *avant garde* thinkers in the holistic scientific-cum-metaphysical field is physicist Danah Zohar who, with the help of her psychiatrist husband, I. N. Marshall, produced a book entitled *The Quantum Self*. Zohar uses her professional knowledge with the confidence that an orthodox scientific training inevitably gives one, to express what many of us have been teaching for some years. On a chilly day in mid-January 1990, when the book was launched at the Oxford Union, a gathering of distinguished physicists, psychiatrists, philosophers and priests, plus two Hassidic rabbis were present. So what was it that Zohar had to say that commanded such an élite gathering of thinkers? In a nutshell her theory is that consciousness is a quantum-physical system, keeping every living thing in constant interaction with others, with nature, with history and with God. Hence its relevance to time.

Zohar sees everyone as physically part of everyone and everything else. Our 'wave aspect' which we have tended to think of in the spiritual context, and our 'particle aspect' which we regard as physical, are in fact one. Therefore, we never actually die since a part of us remains in the quantum consciousness of other people. This makes good sense in the light of Jung's theory of the collective unconscious, and the information gleaned through hypnotic regression, channelling, and other scientifically 'suspicious' forms of psi. Zohar's theory could also be seen to be an answer to the environmentalists' prayer for a holistic approach to nature, and an escape from the spirit/matter dualism that has dominated Western thinking since the Greek philosophers elected to rationalize animism and other ancient beliefs. Like many of us, Zohar believes that all animals and plants have souls, and that quantum physics provides the missing clue to the explanation of consciousness, personality, and the motivating factor behind both of these which has been called among other things the psyche, essence or spirit.

Quantum systems conquer time and space because particles interact over distances without any discernible link (non-locality), and quantum waves of matter contain an infinite range of possibilities (the Uncertainty Principle) until they eventually collapse into conglomerates of particles. Likewise, that consciousness we may term psyche or spirit could also be seen to behave similarly, collapsing occasionally into the particles of matter that we call our bodies. According to Shrödinger's Cat paradox, the two worlds of existence and non-existence, life and death, overlap and only assume a discrete reality when *observed*. As Zohar puts it: 'At the moment of observation, or measurement, previously unobserved electrons which were both waves *and* particles become waves *or* particles.'[2]

Eysenck and Sargent put it another way. Prior to observation, the properties of a particle are *indefinite*, as it covers, or fluctuates over a range of positions or velocities *simultaneously*. This fluctuation is sometimes referred to as 'fuzziness', and it has been speculated by some authorities that the universe itself may, in fact, be fuzzy.[3] They refer to the analogy given by physicist Dr Evan Harris Walker of a person standing in the doorway of a house with one foot inside and the other out: he is both inside and outside the door at the same time. Applied to soma and psyche, this principle conceives of the individual as a continual whole in any or many lives, each incarnation resulting from the not so random perhaps, arrangements of that observable particle which, together with its fuzzy wave aspect, constitutes the whole Essence. It is, therefore, a mistake to view body and spirit/psyche as two separate entities completely detached one from the other, for they are, in fact, a single unit, some parts of which function in the fuzzy world of Outer Time, while others are engaged in the discrete, observable world of Inner Time. This kind of reasoning would also account for the multifaceted aspects of our personalities that surface during psychotherapy or counselling, the Outer Time experiences or sensations tending to impinge on the borders of unreality or fantasy, and the Inner Time 'self' appearing the more rational in terms of the real world.

It has been suggested that the right-brain hemisphere is the link between our conscious selves and Outer Time, whereas our left brains are designed to handle the less abstract and more specific aspects of our present reality. This may indeed be so, but if the right hemisphere receives its information from its fuzzy, or wave quantum aspect (psyche), assuming that the *corpus callosum* has not been severed and the individual is psychologically well integrated, surely the messages that pass between the two hemispheres are sorted out, categorized, and translated into convenient terms of reference by a *combination of the two*.

The third factor to be considered at this juncture is the spiritual maturity of the individual which, if translated into quantum terms, would equate with the number of transformations or changes undergone by the quantum particle/wave peculiar to the person in question. After all, if we are to pay any heed to the mystical teachings of those beliefs that subscribe to the concept of a process of spiritual maturation which runs parallel with somatic evolution, we must concede that some particles have seen more of the universe than others. However, since such speculations are purely philosophical, and therefore lacking in either empirical or theoretical backing, in the final analysis what any of us choose to believe will be decided by our own individual interpretation of what is finite and what is infinite.

Zohar and Marshall claim to be the first to state that consciousness is a quantum-physical system, although they acknowledge the fact that the uncanny resemblance between conscious and quantum processes were also observed by physicist David Bohm, and Professor Fritjof Capra. I could add some more names to that list – thinking people who, in spite of their sensitivity and foresight, sadly lack the academic background that society demands of its great intellects. Zohar's interpretation of quantum theory in terms of the self may well provide the backdrop for future trends in philosophy, parapsychology and religion, but for the present there are too many metaphysical loose ends. And, as far as the average person's understanding of the quantum world is concerned, we might have to wait for that quantum leap that will provide the key to unlocking the consciousness of people worldwide to these and other, more subtle but equally enlightening facts about who we are, and what we are doing in this space-time zone we call the present.

Black Holes, White Holes and the Near-Death Experience

Assuming we do have a quantum identity, how does it work in practice, and to what extent is it influenced by the energy of time? When writing on the subject of black and white holes in an earlier chapter, I could not fail to be struck by the similarity between the parallel universe concept – that we may disappear into a black hole and emerge through a white hole into another dimension or universe – and the numerous near-death experiences (NDE's) that have been catalogued by reliable researchers, such as Dr Lyall Watson (*The Romeo Error*). The descriptions go something like this: a patient has been severely injured in a car crash, or suffered a serious heart attack, or rushed to the hospital with some urgent internal complication, and has found him/herself hovering above the operating surgeon in a life and death situation, and so forth. These experiences appear to share many points in common with time travel under hypnosis, and the ecstatic visions produced either voluntarily or involuntarily during certain ASCs.

Here is a typical example. While in the process of writing this book, I had cause to make a routine visit to my local GP. While faced with the inevitable waiting period, the woman seated beside me went out of her way to engage me in conversation and hasten to assure me that Dr X, who we were both due to see, was something of a miracle worker. It seemed that her husband had suffered a serious heart attack, and it was thanks to Dr X's immediate response to the call, and prompt treatment, that he was alive and fully recovered. However, during the attack her husband had a strange experience. He found himself entering a long, dark tunnel at the end of which was a tiny pinprick of light to which he felt strongly drawn. He was about to make his way towards this light when he heard the doctor's voice quite clearly: 'Come on back, old chap, we're all here for you, you can't go now.' For a moment he hesitated, and much as he longed to proceed he was also aware of his responsibility to those he would be leaving behind. And so, very, reluctantly he turned and made his way back along the tunnel towards the sound of the doctor's voice. As he opened his eyes there was Dr X standing over him: 'You made it back old son, that was some sacrifice, I know, but good for you.'

That was the story as repeated to me by his wife, who was by this time in tears. I asked her why she felt she had to tell me – or did she frequently relate the tale to strangers? She replied that she had never told another soul, only she and the doctor knew. But something seemed to say to her, 'You must tell this lady, it is important.' It was as simple as that.

I was present when a dear friend of mine was regressed under hypnosis and relived a miscarriage in which she was the foetus. There, sure enough, was the dark tunnel of birth, the panic at not being able to find the light at the other end and having to turn back to 'somewhere else where there was lots of light'. On the next occasion when she entered the same tunnel she was able to reach the end, and she was born.

Now, what if death equates with a black hole and birth with a white hole? To put it another way: when we die, that particle which is our quantum self experiences the wave function of timelessness by entering into a time warp (black hole) through which it travels along one of time's energy circuits in much the same way that a particle travels along a particle accelerator. Only in this instance it is time that provides the energy for the acceleration. During this process the quantum self, being in a state of timelessness, is fuzzy or indistinct, meaning it is neither here nor there in terms of earthly reality, but upon leaving the black hole and entering the white hole of rebirth it becomes observable and therefore discrete. In other words, it has passed through a pocket of timelessness (what is broadly referred to in esoteric parlance as the 'subtle dimensions', 'spirit world' and so forth) and once again re-entered one of the time-zones of matter wherein all things exhibit a separate or distinct character.

But since both time and timelessness exist simultaneously, as in the Shrödinger Cat Paradox and Heisenberg's Uncertainty Principle, there is no distinction between spirit and matter other than that that we effect by our own patterns of thinking, which in the majority of cases are created by the conditioning appropriate to the requirements of the society into which we have been born. This being the case, as I have previously intimated, some compartment in our brains must have been designed to accommodate the multidimensional awareness essential to mental stability and non-fragmentation when we are consciously exposed to Outer Time. The evolutionary laser must, therefore, need to be trained on those sleeping neurones to stimulate them into action before the concepts of timelessness and time as an energy can be thoroughly grasped. Only then will we learn how to tap into the infinite power source that courses along the veins of time's circuitry.

Death and Time's Backward Arrow

As we discussed in earlier chapters, the idea that time may travel backwards in some universes would appear to accord with both Newtonian and Einsteinian physics. Scientists speculate that in such a world a person would slowly progress to youth and babyhood, dying, perhaps, at a time that would equate with birth in a forward-moving world. Many readers might well dismiss this idea out of hand, and I would have done the same myself had it not been for a series of odd coincidences that I have come across over the years. The first of these occurred when I was in my twenties. I was attending a study/discussion group in London under the leadership of a man of some learning. Once a month we would be given a point of view and asked to contribute up to ten minutes comment on why we either believed or disbelieved in it.

The subject matter for discussion on one particular week was: 'Life after death, do you or do you not believe in it and what evidence have you to support either view?' One member of the group was a huge, raw-boned Yorkshire man who usually said very little. On this occasion, however, having obviously screwed up his courage to say his piece he blurted out:

> I believe in life after death because I woke up in the middle of the night one night with a strange feeling, as though time had stopped. My wife was sound asleep beside me and didn't seem to be aware of anything. The room seemed to be filled with a strange sort of illumination and there, standing at the foot of my bed, was my late mother. Only she was not as I saw her when she died as an old lady, but as a young teenage lass, like a picture of herself she used to have on the piano.

He was obviously embarrassed at having to tell his tale, and very much on the defensive, as he promptly added: 'And if anyone here wants to call me a liar I'll stand up to him outside, man to man.' Whereupon he started to roll up his sleeves in preparation!

Needless to say, no one said a word. There were a few polite coughs and my companion and I giggled a bit behind our hands (shame on us!). I had completely forgotten this incident until just recently, when I started to have a series of dreams about loved ones I had lost many years ago in their old age, who appeared to me to be getting slowly younger and younger with each successive dream.

Since then, I have questioned other people and discovered that they, too, have experienced a similar phenomenon. For example, it is a common belief among spiritualists that following death, and assuming that the spirit does not become 'lost' (in one of time's black holes?), it goes to the 'Summerland', where it experiences a state of youth, health and happiness beyond our imagination. Perhaps, after disappearing into their black hole of death, our loved ones surface through a white hole of light into a universe in which time's arrow works in reverse, as the scientists theorize? It takes little imagination to figure the pros and cons of that one, but it was just an idea. After all, was it not Swedenborg who claimed that 'in heaven the angels are advancing continually to the springtime of their youth so that the oldest angel appears to be the youngest.'[4] Perhaps he was referring to some spiritual insight into an anti-world or parallel universe?

The Fragment Theory

One cannot write on the subject of metaphysics without indicating some slight preference when it comes to the many ideas and theories concerning the nature of consciousness. Having examined the linear reincarnation premise I found much that did not add up, although for many years I was unable to offer a viable alternative. More study, experience and observation was needed, both from a logical viewpoint and also allowing for the innumerable NDEs and similar out-of-body experiences collected and categorized by researchers of integrity and repute, such as Eysenck and Sargent. It was Lyall Watson who finally provided me with the clue I needed in his 'shattered hologram theory', in which he conceived of the whole Essence (the combined aspects of the quantum self) in terms of a complete hologram which becomes shattered and its fragments *simultaneously* scattered throughout all periods of time and across the limitless dimensions of *all* universes. Since every piece contains the same image as the whole, a fraction (wave/particle?) of the essential Self is retained in every life, and it is that connection with the basic Essence which has given rise to the concept of the 'higher' or transpersonal Self. We are therefore experiencing some lives as youthful fragments, and others in intermediate or mature modes. This theory is at variance with the popular belief espoused by many schools of esoteric and mystical belief which conceive of a series of incarnations through linear or Inner Time, thus allowing for time's forward arrow only. It may well be, as Coveney and Highfield postulate, that we are unable to repeat the same performance in every detail, but perhaps we may be permitted to replay a few of the scenes, avoiding our previous errors, in some other band of time.

Many of my theories come to me in dreams, usually to be confirmed when someone with suitable academic qualifications writes about it later. I recall one occasion in sleep when I was given the analogy of a visit to a cinema. The film I appeared to be forced to watch was pretty ghastly, all blood and guts, suffering and frustration. I experienced a profound sense of relief when the programme ended, the lights went up, and I made my way 'home' in the comfortable knowledge that, much as my adrenalin and tears had flowed during the disturbing performance I had witnessed, it was, after all, only the stuff that the Hollywood dream-machine is made of. The parallel between the distressing film and a similarly disquieting earthly life, and the relief at leaving the cinema when the show was over (death?), struck me forcibly, and I found myself asking what prompted me to spend my money (time-energy) on such a nasty epic in the first place. But how many times have I heard even ardent believers in reincarnation complaining in disgruntled tones, 'I must have been crazy to have chosen this rotten life!'

Progress through the highways and byways of linear time is often accompanied by distress and suffering. This is because when we are encapsulated within the confines of matter we are pushing against time's energy, an occupation that is both abrasive and exhausting. According to the philosophy of the ancient Egyptian Ammonites, which has been kept alive over the centuries by members of that tribe:

> It is not so much a mastery of Chaos, as it is of learning to manifest what one has chosen to the extent one is able. This depends on the strength of the will and the desire to have an identity more than facing

what is coming. Again, the place to begin this mastery of one manifestation is with the Self. The linear progression becomes the way in which one progresses the Self in terms of awareness, the direction, curvature, or angle of the line being of no importance as long as it is useful to the aim.[5]

As a recent student of this philosophy I have been amazed at its profundity, in-depth knowledge, and comprehension of the true nature of the universe. It could be said of these people that their ancestors taught Chaos Science centuries before Europe was civilized. In fact, they claim that their information, which is considerably more extensive than this single example I have quoted, goes back to 12,000 BC and earlier, which suggests that 'world knowledge' has, in fact, been experiencing an ouroboric (see Ouroborus p. 38) decline, from the nadir of which it is at last ascending.

Conjecture as to the reality or unreality of time is by no means exclusive to the scientific profession, however. The great Eastern thinkers, notable Shankara, the teacher of the Advaita Vedanta, proposed that the present is void of reality and therefore only an illusion or 'maya',[6] while in more recent times Baron von Reichenbach, who carried out extensive researches into hypnotism in the nineteenth century and who was one of the first scientific observers to note the auric energy fields surrounding all living things, also commented that 'the morrow has already occurred in the same sense as yesterday has. . . Only the totality of all causes permits an inference concerning the future.'[7] It seems we still have much to learn, or relearn perhaps?

Time, Individuation and the Universal Brain

Jung defined the process of individuation as the uniting of the anima and animus (masculine and feminine elements) in the personality to produce a state of stability and balance within the individual psyche. It could also be interpreted as a psychological evolutionary process which enables an individual to become a singular, discrete and balanced being in his or her own right, a 'coming to selfhood' or an awareness of cosmic identity. Non-individuation could therefore be likened to the autonomous response of those parts of the nervous system that function without conscious control, so that prior to individuation we are simply cells in a vast brain which controls the motor (material) side of our lives while we are functioning within the wavebands of matter. Some philosophers and metaphysicians have therefore tended to see the individuation process as the *raison d'être* behind the venture of the psyche into the discrete worlds of Inner Time.

The question that naturally follows is: does individuation have any effect on our comprehension of time? Bearing in mind that the qualities associated with the left-brain hemisphere are often seen as being more masculine than feminine, while the reverse applies to the right-brain hemisphere, are we not also talking here in terms of the ability to rationalize the abstract, which is surely an essential mental prerequisite for anyone wishing to learn to negotiate the energized circuits of time? We are told that the instinctive faculties in primitive man were more developed than our own; the Australian aborigines, for example, had and still have an understanding of timelessness that many educated people find difficult to grasp. How is this explained in terms of cerebral functioning?

There are several areas of the brain the functions of which are still being debated by medical scientists. For example:

The Hindbrain The rhombencephalon, that portion of the embryonic brain from which the metencephalon, myelencephalon, and subsequently the cerebellum, pons and medula oblongata develop. The hindbrain's association with primeval development has prompted some researchers to link it with the collective unconscious [Outer Time?] on the one hand, and certain instinctive awareness patterns on the other.

The Limbic System Which is located in a semicircle in the middle of the brain and governs basic activities such as self-preservation, reproduction and the expression of fear and rage. A connection has also been observed between the system and functions of memory and dreams, which has prompted some researchers to allocate the exact location of the mind or psyche within the limbic system.

The Thalamus Greek for 'hidden chamber'. This is referred to by some scientists as the 'old brain', or 'reptile brain'. It consists of two egg-shaped masses which relay nerve impulses from all the senses, except smell, to the cerebral cortex. Psychoanalyst Dr Eric Berne, attributes ESP and other psi abilities to an exceptionally sensitive thalamus, and the late Dr Alexis Carrel wrote: 'Normally, the uncanny powers of the thalamus are smothered and overridden by the cortex of the brain. As science lifts the curtain on this mystery out of our primitive past we begin to understand that we are barely tapping our potentialities. And the certainty that the sixth sense exists makes the investigation of these long-dormant faculties of the mind an urgent and exciting task.[8]

Metaphysics joins with psychology in acknowledging several aspects of human consciousness to which a variety of names have been given over the years. The most popular classification is probably the threefold Instinctive, Rational and Intuitive, the former being ascribed to either the hindbrain or the thalamus, and the latter to the limbic system. Recent researches have indicated a connection between limbic activity and the subatomic worlds, while the association between rational deduction and the left hemisphere of the brain is obvious.

From the aforegoing we may observe that the comprehension and negotiation of the various aspects of time are well within the limits of the human brain. But because many of us have not individuated, either we are still functioning on a primitive, autonomous system, totally unaware of our real potential, or we are being manipulated by some external mind which takes care of us until we awaken to the fact that we can do these things for ourselves, in much the same way that a pregnant mother handles the functions of the child she is carrying until it is born. Perhaps the time for our birth into the consciousness of cosmic reality is fast approaching, and after we have suffered and triumphed over its pangs we will comprehend the realities of time, with all that this implies.

Time, Antimatter and the Psyche

In a recent conversation with a student of mine, I was asked whether I could effect a metaphysical parallel with the matter/antimatter phenomenon in which a particle is cancelled out by its antiparticle, the only evidence of the former existence of both being a small pocket of energy (gamma ray) deposited during the process (see Chapter 4). According to Paul Davies, scientists are puzzled by the fact that the universe consists of almost one hundred per cent matter, antimatter being conspicuous by its absence. My metaphysical answer to this would be that while we are chained to the worlds of physical existence (what the Buddhists refer to as being chained to the Wheel of Karma, or in my terms of reference going round and round or up and down in the same time circuit), we are unlikely to meet up with our antiself or antiparticle. Consequently, our particle/wave aspects, being unable to make contact with their other half, remain intact.

However, sooner or later our psyches will be sufficiently mature or cosmically conscious to enable us to take our leave of the worlds of matter (those circuits of time that are specifically concerned with the material/physical condition), and it will be then that our antiparticle will put in an appearance. Our particle/wave aspect will subsequently experience annihilation, there being no further need for it to manifest in that form or at that frequency, leaving only the gamma mark of its studentship in the school register of physical life. The basic Essence, which could be equated to the complete hologram prior to its shattering, possibly retains the antiparticle until such times as its twin has returned from its meanderings through the material universes and is sufficiently enlightened, or cosmically conscious, to merit a reuniting. This theory is presented in several mystical teachings, from the Gnostic Christos/Sophia story to the Dogon belief in the separated Nommo twin's eternal quest for reunion with its celestial partner. Upon eventually encountering its mate, it will experience a transcendental individuation, and being thus complete as a metaphysical consciousness, it will take its leave of the worlds of matter for good. It is from this principle that the ancients derived their concept of the androgyn, from which united state we each originated and to which we will eventually return.

Time and the 'Sixth Sense'

Assuming our 'selves' to be quantum factors, some parts of which (the wave aspect, according to Zohar) enjoy a state of consciousness in Outer Time while others (the particle aspect) experience the observable reality of the worlds of matter, it is surely logical to suppose that our non-locality wave aspect is able to bring about contact with the wave aspects of all other life forms? Quantum mechanics has shown that under certain conditions a pair of particles cannot (in a way that can be properly defined mathematically) be thought of as being totally independent of each other, even when separated by a great distance. Likewise, experiments carried out at the University of Montpelier, Vermont have offered substantial scientific evidence that trees communicate with each other. Add to this Rupert Sheldrake's 'morphic resonance' theory, and the picture becomes even clearer.

The distinguished physicist, the late Lord Kelvin, when asked whether he believed in a sixth sense, momentarily startled his contemporaries a century ago by saying that he did. He was not referring to occult phenomena, of which he was deeply distrustful, but he surmised that we may well have an in-built ability to perceive magnetic fields. Recent research has confirmed Kelvin's idea, while it has also been discovered that we are affected by radiation, X-rays, gamma rays and many other cosmic phenomena.

Eminent professors have waxed and waned in their belief in an extra sense of the psi variety. John Taylor, for example, was convinced temporarily by the evidence of his own experiments, but recanted on the grounds that it could not be explained in terms of forces known to science. Professor John Hasted, on the other hand, produced a wealth of evidence for psychokinesis in his book *The Metal Benders*, although this is but one aspect of the whole psi phenomenon. The question that must bother many scientists (and metaphysicians, for that matter) is, if all these inanimate objects, stationary life forms and minute particles are in the communication business, why and when were *our* lines cut? The answer is, of course, that they are not. So, why the big mystery?

My belief, which is shared by many others of my persuasion and not a few scientists, is that our spiritual/physical, superconscious/conscious selves (or wave/particle quantum aspects, if you prefer) have become unnaturally separated. A subtle bisection has taken place and we have been virtually split in two. This has been achieved by centuries of negative programming from philosophical, sociological and religious sources, the latter influence probably being the predominating factor with most of us. The few who have exhibited tendencies to communicate with either their own wave aspects, or other intelligences operating in the wavebands of Outer Time, have either fared well or badly according to the prevailing tides of philosophical or priestly dominance. In the ancient world, for example, sibyls were honoured and no emperor, king or leader worth his salt would dream of engaging in battle without consulting such a person. As the tides of Christianity swept across the world, the accusing finger of the Inquisitor found its mark and millions of innocent people met horrendous ends because they exhibited propensities for psi or ESP. The witch hunt continues to this day, with anyone even vaguely concerned with mysticism, metaphysics, and even psychology and science, being accused by religious fundamentalists of being 'in league with Satan' (whatever that might mean). Any regime or faith that does not allow the mind space in which to expand its knowledge and awareness, and which denies the existence of established facts, such as the age of our planet and how it came into being, needs to be questioned in the name of freedom and free will. Agreed, people have the right to their own beliefs, but when it comes to foisting them onto others, there should be room for a come-back. I think it was a recent American President who was once heard to remark, 'Everyone else's freedom stops six inches from my face'.

Time and Free Will

The question of free will has provided a challenge for many great thinkers, past and present, notably the French philosopher Henri Louis Bergson (1859–1941). The central theme of Professor Bergson's philosophy is the opposition between the life force and the material world, which he chose to expound in his well-known book *Time and Free Will*. He also assigned an important role to intuition, as opposed to rational intelligence, in man's perception of reality. Bergson wrote of:

> ... two different selves, one of which is, as it were, the external projection of the other, its spatial and, so to speak, social representation. We reach the former by deep introspection, which leads us to grasp our inner states as living things, constantly *becoming*, as states not amenable to measure, which permeate one another and of which the succession in duration has nothing in common with juxtaposition in homogenous space. But the moments at which we thus grasp ourselves are rare, and that is just why we are rarely free. The greater part of the time we live outside ourselves, hardly perceiving anything of ourselves but our own ghost, a colourless shadow which pure duration projects into homogenous space. Hence our life unfolds in space rather than in time; we live for the external world rather than for ourselves; we speak rather than think; we 'are acted' rather than act ourselves. To act freely is to recover possession of oneself, and to get back into pure duration.[9]

In this passage Bergson sums up both the external manipulation of the non-individuated person who is only half awake, and the dichotomy between the conscious and superconscious selves which is seen by some as having resulted from the imposition of the wills of the few over the many. Therefore, how much free will do we actually have once we are incarnate? Opinions naturally vary. One esoteric school of thought subscribes to the idea that our free will is exercised prior to entering incarnation. When questioned on this very subject, Erwin Schrödinger, whose theoretical cat is famed, wrote:

> Could perhaps the declared *indeterminacy* allow *free will* to step into the gap in the way that *free will determines* those events which the Law of Nature leaves undetermined? This hope is, at first sight, obvious and understandable.[10]

Schrödinger, in fact, commented fairly extensively on the subject in a paper entitled 'Why Not Talk Physics', which appears in the previously mentioned book *Quantum Questions*.

The deterministic view of the universe inclines to the idea of a pre-set pattern in all things, which is often seen as confirmed in astrology, the position of the planets at birth being the deciding factor as to what is likely to take place in any particular life. On the other hand, many astrologers view the birth chart simply in terms of a set of tools appropriate to the blueprint (karma) of that life, which we may either cherish and use with care, or neglect and take the karmic consequences. After all, we do have the free will to say no to drugs, alchohol and foodstuffs that are guaranteed to affect our health adversely. And, we may choose to be kind and caring or vicious and brutal although, according to Bergson's observations, most of us fail to exercise this right simply because we are not sufficiently conscious to think beyond our own immediate needs.

Another deciding factor as to how we may or may not choose, as the case may be, to exercise our thinking powers in the selection of any belief, discipline, or course of action is the prevailing trends within those current collectives into which we have been born, or to which we have chosen to assign ourselves. The psychology of collective behaviour is a subject I have already commented on in other books, but as far as time and free will are concerned, suffice it to say that many people fail to free themselves from the encapsulating and sometimes suffocating bonds of collectivism. Instead of exercising their individuality, they think collectively, whereas the individuated personality has made the necessary break with the crowd, and established his or her own expression of free will, thus coming to terms with time's energies. The phenomenon of collective thinking and behaviour has been observed and commented upon by many eminent scientists and psychologists, notably Lyall Watson, Elias Canetti and Rupert Sheldrake.

And so it would appear that time's clock chimes metaphorically on the hour, reminding us of the chosen blueprint for this particular life at specific intervals only. What we do in the sixty minutes in between is up to our free will – assuming we choose to make use of that privilege. And should our pre-life (wave-self?) decree us to effect a major decision, or even vacate our bodies at a given time, time's chimes will toll appropriately. There is a lot more I could say on this subject, but since I have covered it in some detail in *The Psychology of Healing*, readers interested in knowing more about disease and karma, for example, are referred to that work.

Time Bodies

Students of esoterica have tended to use a set of semantics that often annoy scientists, although when it comes to the quantum worlds, in particular, both are basically stating the same things. In my youth I was told that the physical body had etheric, astral, mental, causal and spiritual counterparts, which it needed in order to negotiate the many planes of existence outside the boundaries of the frozen energy we call matter. In fact, a whole series of these subtle 'bodies' made their appearance in various mystical teachings, notably those of ancient Egypt – the *Sahu*, *Khu*, *Ba*, and *Ka*, for example.

I have never believed in the generally accepted metaphysical view of these divisions, and have tended to see them purely as terms of reference appropriate to the manifestations of the psyche in other dimensions, time-zones or parallel universes, as the case may be. However, the ancient Egyptian Ammonite teachings on the subject do appear to make sense in the light of evidence from the quantum worlds, so no doubt there are differentials in space-time, just as there are distinctions here on Earth. Since we are all individuals that individuality is not likely to change because our wave-selves are either off in some distant galaxy, or communicating with the monoliths at Stonehenge!

What I can conceive of is that within the universe there are an infinite range of frequencies. I am not referring here to the visible universe associated with the Big Bang, but rather all those subtle dimensions that do not appear as discrete to us (and consequently are dismissed by dialectical thinkers), but which our transcendental selves, or quantum-wave aspects, might conceivably be able to negotiate.

Where I am in agreement with the Ammonites, however, is that the extent to which we are able to exercise this prerogative depends on our degree of cosmic awareness or, as the Ammonites would say, whether, by our deeds, we have earned a *Khu*, *Sahu*, or *Ba*. In the final analysis it really all adds up to the same thing.

The distinguishing factor between these aforementioned universal multifrequencies would appear to be speed, the particles at some levels moving faster than those at others. Now I have no scientific evidence to support this theory, but it strikes me that the faster an atom or particle moves the finer its frequency and the more imperceptible it becomes. Therefore, a very high degree of sensitivity would be required to make contact with the faster-moving frequencies, while a really secure union between the right and left brain hemispheres (individuation?) would be a prerequisite to the accurate conveyance of information from these finer wavebands to the denser structures of matter associated with the 'real' world. Add to this the problem of semantics (how can we express the abstract without suitable terms of reference) and it becomes easy to see why so much gobbledy-gook is handed out in the name of psychism and religious inspiration. Science has proved most obliging in the more recent additions to its vocabularies, especially in the areas of computer and chaos studies, I find.

It makes sound psychological sense to assume that a devotee of a particular faith or school of philosophical thought, when undergoing an ASC, is bound to relate his or her experience to the tenets of that faith. For example, a Pagan faced with a 'vision' of a beautiful lady would immediately associate it with the Earth Mother, Isis, or Demeter. If he or she were of the Wiccan persuasion, it would be Aradia or Artemis. A Catholic would swear he or she had been visited by the Virgin Mary, while a Hindu would avow it was Sarasvati who deigned to make her presence felt. So, it seems, we colour the canvas of our Outer Time experiences with the oils of material convenience, which is all well and good until someone's 'convenience' is suddenly thrust upon everyone else in the form of a set dogma. Which brings us round to that thorny polemic – orthodox religion.

Religion and Space-time

The Egyptian Ammonites define religion as 'in actuality, a regime of daily actions, thoughts and exercises performed to assist one in the achievement of one's selected goals. . .'[11] although they are also careful to emphasize that they view religion not so much as a group participation of ceremony, but as both an individual and group experience, with the emphasis on the individual. How different from the many participants in popular Western religious ceremonies who repeat their prayers in parrot fashion, with neither care nor interest in the origins or meaning of the texts they employ. All religions were founded at some point in time, and if anyone cares to study the historical backgrounds concurrent with that formation the reason behind their successes becomes apparent. But time marches on, and world circumstances change. Although certain basic principles may well apply in the regions of Aldebaran, Sirius or Orion, the odds against their conforming to the rules and regulations laid down centuries ago on Earth are minimal, to say the least.

The mention of religion inevitably evokes the question of where 'God' fits in to all this. In a recent article in the *Guardian* (28 May,

1990), under the regular column 'Face to Faith', psychological consultant Dr James Hemming explored some of the possibilities of what we might find when we finally step into space proper, while at the same time posing some penetrating questions for the leaders of the various world religions. He commented on the fact that the mathematical probabilities of life elsewhere have been shortening and the main arguments against the existence of extraterrestrial life slowly collapsing. The replicating molecule is now seen as robust and likely to flourish wherever conditions are right for it. Sir James Lovelock, and those who share his views, maintain that as early life evolved it produced the atmosphere it needed to foster its further development, thus putting paid to the idea that life cannot develop in adverse planetary conditions. The conclusion, therefore, has to be that life is potential throughout the cosmos, and that it is likely to emerge in a variety of habitats and in many different forms.

Bearing in mind the persecutions that took place when the discoveries of Copernicus, Kepler and Galileo showed the Earth in a different perspective than that favoured by the theologians, Dr Hemming (and many others among us, no doubt) naturally wonder how present-day theology will cope with the idea that the Earth is not a unique place under the privileged guidance of 'the One and Only Deity', which some religions have believed it to be for so many centuries. Hemming discussed the matter with the representatives of several major religions. One curate was perplexed as to how other worlds might be seen in the 'redemption' context, while another representative of the Christian faith opined that perhaps Earth, having been selected for divine revelation, had the responsibility of carrying the 'good news' round and about the galaxy, and elsewhere in the universe come to that.

The Roman Catholic view centres around the idea that Earth, being a fallen planet needs redemption, so the necessity of such a visitation on other worlds would depend on whether they were fallen or not. A Jewish Rabbi saw these other worlds as 'adding to the greater glory of God', and added that the Jewish faith had always been cosmically orientated, anyway. Nor did he have any problem with the Jews being the chosen race, as this only referred to a specific task here on Earth. The Islamic representative saw no problem either, and joined with the Rabbi in proclaiming that the Islamic faith had always been cosmic in outlook, although Hemming did rather wonder whether Islam could accept different versions of the Prophet manifesting in different worlds.

Hemming concluded his article with the words:

> Whatever solutions to contemporary questions are exchanged in the seclusion of colleges and seminaries, these are often not shared with the ordinary people, who are left with traditional dogma while a new view of the cosmos opens up before them with which the dogma is not a good fit. The solution, surely is to accept that much dogma is atavistic, and to turn instead to the positive teaching of the great religions.
>
> For example, the gospels, pruned of their ugly, hell-fire interpolations, are rich in caring and wisdom for a generation that has the inescapable responsibility of preserving planet Earth. Is it not time to stop confronting dogma with dogma and to unite in raising the quality of life on our small, beautiful island in space?[12]

Brave words, Dr Hemming, but it will, I fear, take more than reason to shift the foundations of the walls of dogma, especially in the hearts and minds of those for whom such inflexible and extreme beliefs form an essential psychological prop.

Time and God

Sir James Jeans referred to the universe as a Great Thought; other scientists have seen it in terms of a time machine, or a giant computer. Assuming there to be an Intelligence at the heart of all life, what is Its nature? This is something that none of us really knows for sure. It has been viewed as a dualism – Chaos and Order in continual conflict – which accords, to a degree, with our knowledge of the quantum worlds; the Chaos aspect equating with the Uncertainty Principle or wave aspect, and the Order with the observable manifestation of the particle or particles. (But then, so also does time! More of that in the next chapter.) Whatever or wherever *It* is, it seems logical to assume that *It* must contain, or at least have instant access to, all there is within the infinity of universes.

As a child I used to wonder why God was always referred to in the masculine context. *He* was, we children were told, our Father. 'But what about our mother?' I would ask. 'There is no "mother", only God the Father', I was told. 'But that is illogical', I protested. For which statement I received both punishment and penance and was told I had the makings of an 'evil mind'. In other words, I had the temerity to question established beliefs. Feminists are convinced that the deity is female, for which theory they submit a great deal more logical evidence than the orthodox bodies can offer to support the masculine idea. But in the final analysis, none of us really knows, and I for one am content to wait and see what happens. However, I have no fear of death and when Time knocks on my door I will enter my 'black hole' imbued with curiosity and intent upon following my old nanny's advice: 'Hope for the best, expect the worst, and take what's coming!'

Endnotes

1. *Reader's Digest Great Illustrated Dictionary* Vol. 2., p. 1070.
2. D. Zohar, *The Quantum Self*, p. 24.
3. H. Eysenck and C. Sargent, *Explaining the Unexplained*, p. 139.
4. A. Tomas, *Beyond the Time Barrier*, p. 30.
5. *The Ammonite Teachings* (unpublished).
6. Tomas, *op. cit.* p. 30.
7. *Ibid.* p. 44.
8. M. Hope, *The Psychology of Ritual*, p. 291.
9. H. L. Bergson, *Time and Free Will*, pp. 231–2.
10. *Quantum Questions*, ed. K. Wilber, p. 80.
11. *The Ammonite Teachings* (unpublished).
12. The *Guardian* 28 May 1990.

9
Time as an Energy

The chance aspects of events – alternative worlds of probability – quantum mechanics and statistical probability. All are inextricably intertwined...
JOHN GRIBBIN[1]

In the previous chapters of this book I have mentioned a few of the physical, psychological, preternatural and transcendental manifestations of time's energies without defining explicitly their actual nature. When considering the possibility of a Grand Unified Theory, gravitational, electromagnetic and nuclear fields are inevitably mentioned, but surely each of these employs time during its various processes? Before arriving at any definite conclusions, let us take a closer look at the more obvious effects of time on matter, and also how its energies manifest in those less perceptible but equally relevant areas of the subconscious and superconscious.

Time and Matter

During the nine months from conception to birth a tiny embryo develops into a new human being. Likewise with all other life forms, the gestation periods naturally varying with each species. Once born we experience the process of growth and, good health permitting, we swing with time's pendulum to the stability extremity, which endows us with the strength and vigour of full maturity. Now, quantum mechanics asserts that all particles are in fact waves and that the higher the energy of a particle, the shorter the length of the corresponding wave.[2] Translated into metaphysical language, it could be telling us that the more materialistic we are, the less we are likely to become aware of our higher or transcendental selves. After all, the 'rational' or middle period of our lives, which usually corresponds with our prime physical (particle-orientated?) days, is often the time when we are most

162

absorbed in worldly matters. The pendulum, however, having reached its 'order' extremity, then begins its backward swing towards chaos. The sages of ancient times were quick to note this in their observation that childhood and early youth coincided with the development of our instinctive faculties, maturity and mid-life with our rational, and old age with the intrusion of intuition, genuine mystics being the exceptions to the rule. Feminine-orientated societies translated these phases in terms of the Maiden, Mother and Crone.

From the moment we are born we encounter time's energy, against which we are obliged to push in order to survive. If we fail to do so, then death automatically takes us back into time-lessness until we locate a 'white hole' through which to surface once more into the world of matter. And so we continue our struggles, and for a while our encounter with time invigorates us. Like the young warrior fresh from the field of victory, we eat, drink and rejoice in the full bloom of our youth and ensuing maturity. But there inevitably comes a time when we weary of the continual thrust and time slowly takes us over, gradually loosening the molecular structure of our bodies into that mode we refer to as 'old age'. And then entropy, time's strategy-wise old General, eventually triumphs and the molecular structure, atoms and particles of which our bodies have been made are returned to the universe for recycling, and our psyche, or particle/wave aspect, once again enters a state of timelessness. Whichever way you care to look at it, time is the predominating factor in the whole process.

Time's energies vary in intensity according to physical circumstances, the main power sources considered by science as suitable candidates for Grand Unified Theory (GUT) – gravity, nuclear energy and electrodynamics – being the deciding factors as to the life span of matter at any given period. Lederman and Schramm propose a fourfold division – see illustration on p. 22. We have seen how the astronaut, suspended in his or her spaceship well outside a planet with a strong gravitational field, could age more slowly than his son who descends to the surface of that planet. Likewise, when nuclear or electromagnetic energies are allowed to run amok their effect on life can be devastating. But consider also how useful any of these energy sources can be when properly harnessed. Let us therefore think of these manifestations of energy as aspects of time's 'beingness', senior officers in time's army, or time's servants who, like the Greek goddesses Themis and Nemesis, effect both its justice and retribution. After all, transgression against the laws of nature sooner or later evokes the wrath of time, as the history of our planet will attest.

For the more technically minded, it is worth mentioning at this stage that not all scientists are happy about the validity of quantum mechanics as a universal role model, either in relation to time or physics generally. Prominent among these is the Oxford mathematician Roger Penrose, who bases his scepticism on a detailed study of black holes and cosmology. Penrose writes:

> There is something deeply unsatisfactory about the present conventional formulation of quantum mechanics, incorporating as it does two quite distinct modes of evolution: one completely deterministic, in accordance with the Schrödinger equation, the other a probablistic collapse. And it is a great weakness of the conventional theory that one is not told when one form of evolution is supposed to give way to the other, beyond the fact that it must always take place sometime prior to an observation being made . . . if I am right, then Schrödinger's equation will have to be modified in some way. [3]

Penrose also introduces a radical new proposal that gravity plays a part in the collapse of the wave function. I find no difficulty in accepting this premise, nor does it interfere with the metaphysical concept of time as an energy, in fact, it enhances it. The effect of gravitation is surely to emphasize matter. Therefore, the stronger the gravitation, the wider the gap between particle and wave function which, when translated into metaphysical or psychological correspondences, simply tells us that while time encapsulates us in the world of matter, the denser that matter the less likely we are to be able to contact our transcendental selves. But since time also decrees that we need to experience in a variety of densities, there must obviously be periods within our evolutionary cycles when this isolation is necessary to our holistic development.

On the subject of time, Ilya Prigogine commented: 'Have we reached some unity of knowledge or is science broken into various parts based on contradictory premises? Such questions will lead us to a deeper understanding of the role of time.'[4] Like Penrose, Prigogine also questions certain quantum theories. In putting forward a proposal to modify the microscopic laws of physics, he points out that '. . .the inherent time symmetry of the laws of mechanics imply that they will never, as formulated, account for the time-assymetric growth of complexity.'[5] Instead, he suggested a modification of the laws of dynamics involving the introduction of an 'intrinsic indeterminism reminiscent of quantum mechanics, but going beyond, in a way that is explicitly time-assymetric'[6] In simple language, the chaos associated with the subatomic world is eventually self-organizing, although, during the duration of this process, it may be viewed as either or both symmetric and asymmetric in relation to time's arrow. Time, therefore, rules *all worlds*, from the observable to the esoteric, since it obviously controls the swing of the chaos-order pendulum.

Time rules our lives via our clocks, which in turn rely upon the movements of Earth in relation to its parent star, the energies of which are also time-oriented in that it, like us, is under the command of 'General' Entropy! It is inevitably time that decides whether we manifest in discrete particle form (the material world), or remain in the wave-limbo of timelessness although, assuming there to be a certain frequency at which all time is one, it is only when we become encapsulated in a distinct pocket of time in which gravity decrees us to be solid that we are able to *observe* ourselves and the universe around us as similarly solid or discrete. Change the frequency, and all is once again Unity. Fritjof Capra, who has been responsible for opening the minds of both scientists and laymen alike to the concept of the oneness of all, wrote in his bestseller *The Tao of Physics*:

> The most important characteristic of the Eastern world view – one could almost say the essence of it – is the awareness of the unity and mutual interrelation of all things and events, the experience of all phenomena in the world as manifestations of a basic oneness. All things are seen as interdependent and inseparable parts of this cosmic whole; as different manifestations of the same ultimate reality.[7]

The Dimensions of Time

In recent years several theories have been advanced regarding the possibility of there being considerably more dimensions to time than those with which we are already familiar. A few years back, eleven or twelve were postulated by some researchers, but since I have so far been unable to trace the specific papers for qualification such premises must, for the time being anyway, remain in the realms of pure speculation. Although states of timelessness, such as those believed to exist in black holes, might not be seen as manifesting any recognizable energy fields, this could not be farther from the truth. According to my deductions time, like all other energy sources, functions in sine-waves, its accelerated or particle mode being observable, its decelerated or wave mode, seen as 'no time', or a state of timelessness, being simply a less perceptible (or imperceptible) aspect of its energies.

The point at which time effects a drastic change of frequencies and one mode gives way to the other, as represented by the central line, could possibly equate with the speed of light, or 'warp speed', as the sci-fi writers like to call it.

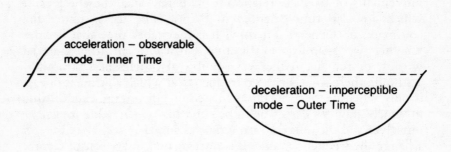

Time and Mind

Mind and consciousness are two terms that are guaranteed to irritate the mechanistically orientated scientist. Likewise, the use of the term 'energy' in relation to time, which is certainly contentious as far as the physical sciences are concerned, since it obviously conveys a different meaning to the physicist than it does to the medical practitioner, metaphysician or layman. And yet, are these distinctions valid if viewed overall? I think not. Scientists may define energy in strict physical terms, but there are also the personal energies emitted by individuals, animals, plants and so forth, as well as the psycho-kinetic (pk) and allied energy fields established by parapsychologists. As I choose to view it, all are the same thing functioning at different frequencies, but to preserve my face from the proverbial egg I am happy to acknowledge the accepted distinctions, and admit that my employment of the term is not strictly orthodox. The same also applies to the central hypothesis of this work which, while it may make sound meta-physical sense, does not fall within the accepted framework of physical science. After all, if time as an energy could be easily proven within the present structure of science there would be no need for this book, and some satisfied scientist would, no doubt, be proudly displaying his or her Nobel prize.

As regards 'mind' and 'consciousness', I am inclined to lean on the conclusions of quantum theorist Dr Evan Harris Walker, who sees space as inhabited by an unlimited number of interconnected conscious entities responsible for the detailed workings of the universe ... 'Consciousness,' he says, 'is everywhere.' Rupert Sheldrake's concept of invisible morphogenetic (form-creating fields) that serve to connect similar things together *instantaneously* across time and space (see also pages 42 and 136) would also seem to be consistent with this theory, as would Bell's Theorem, and the work of Chew and Bohm. Metaphysicians and parapsychologists have likewise conceived of the speed of thought exceeding that of light, while experiments in precognitive telepathy have emphasized the fact that the human mind is capable of negotiating time's circuitry.

Thought is, as I have previously suggested, an energy in its own right, over which we have the propensity to exert a controlling influence. The fact that mind can impress matter has been proven under laboratory conditions on many occasions. In addition to being able to affect inanimate objects, electrical circuits and so forth, it can also influence its own body and brain, and the bodies and brains of others.

I have heard both humans and other conscious forms of physical life likened to protons and neutrons, and the thoughts they emit to the smaller particles, many of which have yet to be discovered, but each of which carries a energy charge of some kind. Therefore, being the masters of our thoughts and exerting the kind of mental self-discipline that allows for an easier and calmer negotiation of life's ups and downs can help us to swim with time's tides instead of fighting against them and exhausting ourselves unnecessarily.

Since the energy of thought or mind can regulate time, so also must time be an energy in *its* own right. After all, although we still have a lot to learn when it comes to the manipulation of gravity, we have mastered the control and regulation of the electromagnetic and to an extent the nuclear fields, so why not time? But first of all, we must understand what kind of an energy potential we are dealing with and therein lies the enigma.

What we do know is that time functions according to a set of basic rules, call them 'cosmic laws' if you like. One of these laws decrees that everything operates best within its own frequency. So, while the emphasis is on our particle or physical aspect, anything relative to that mode needs to be expressed in physical terms in order to be understood. Therefore, when our wave aspect, (psyche, transpersonal self or whichever term we may choose to employ) wishes to effect some change in relation to its particle aspect, it is obliged to do so via the frequencies relative to that particle. (Before some irate physicist jumps on me, let me hasten to say that I am now speaking metaphysically.) This is one of the reasons why psi is difficult to pin down in physical terms – one is dealing strictly with frequencies involving non-locality that do not coincide with those of the material world, and therefore cannot be categorized according to normal physical measurement.

As someone who, for my sins, has a good line of communication with my own wave aspects, I can fully understand why discarnate entities (aspects of one's own 'wave-self' and/or the 'wave-selves' of others) always need someone at the *earthly* level to carry out their ideas, instructions or inventions. I am also given to understand that it is extremely frustrating when intelligences from a parallel universe attempt to communicate with those of a different waveband, particularly if the frequencies of the former are considerably faster than those of the latter. I tried to highlight this in my narration of a particular dream sequence in Chapter 3. Should there be a complementary resonance, then the problem is considerably lessened.

Coming back to time's energies, aside from their obvious manifestations which we take as part of everyday existence, how can we make use of these in the same way that we employ electricity, for example? Now, although we cannot *see* electricity, we know it exists because we can observe *its effects*, Likewise, primitive peoples were also able to witness its energies as manifest in thunder and lightning, but lacking a rational understanding of what they saw, they ascribed the phenomena to some supernatural agency. And so the gods of thunder and lightning appeared in every pantheon: Thor, Donner, Zeus, Indra, and so forth. It was not until electricity was recognized as a force through its display that scientists were able to identify and harness it, and in so doing discover the magnitude of the whole electromagnetic field.

We know that time exists, because we see the evidence for it all around us, just as primitive peoples were fully aware of the effects of thunder and lightning since they were able to observe them. We are back to our 'observation mode' again – the physical universe *is* because it is observable. Only theoretical physics conceives of the wave function that presupposes the unobservable. We may surmise that in the final analysis it will be ultimately in theoretical physics that we nail down the time-energy factor. On the other hand, physicists are continually learning more about the behaviour of minute particles so the energy patterns of the microcosmic may well provide the answer to the overall time-energy circuits of the macrocosmic, although I rather suspect they will be in for a few shocks when they eventually do. 'As above, so below', as the Emerald Tables tell us.

For many years scientists believed the atom was the smallest particle in existence and totally indestructible. To argue against such dogmatism would have constituted a heresy against physical science. Being downright heretical I am going to suggest that there is no limit to the size of particles or the speed at which they may travel. Smaller and smaller ones will continue to pop up as technology provides scientists with more refined equipment. And that also goes for the size of the universe itself – time expands its energies in *all* directions. I do not doubt that many men of science have already arrived at the same conclusions as myself concerning time, but lack either the right equation, or necessary equipment to prove it at present. But as rapid improvements in technology gradually allow them to widen their horizons, especially in relation to the Uncertainty Principle and non-locality wherein lie the real clues to the positive nature of time, we shall be in for a few surprises.

The double pyramid, with one pinnacle pointing downwards and the other upwards provides a simple model, the central meeting point representing the worlds of matter and the two extremes, the subatomic world and the expanding universe respectively, the upper and lower pinnacles inferring infinity *at either end*. Or, there is always the recognized symbol for infinity, which speaks for itself!

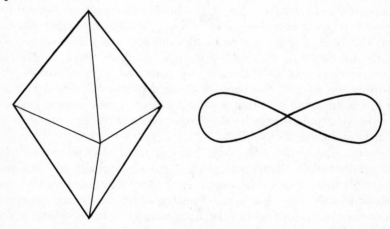

The Metaphysical Manifestations of Time's Energy

Metaphysically, time is postulated as being a positive force which is closely connected with the transmutation of energy into matter. Thought is also a creative energy that interacts with matter to produce form at the Inner Time level. Following the passage of time that leads to death, that form is discarded and the intelligence it housed resumes its existence in Outer Time, or is catapulted into some parallel universe or alternative world. If the former, it is no longer subject to the particular sine-wave of time applicable to our physical universe, and if the latter, it may well find itself faced with a completely different manifestation of time's energies.

As physical evolution slowly perfects its vehicles, more ego-energy is able to manifest through it until it is ready to accommodate a mutation (quantum leap). This may or may not be accompanied by physical-type phenomena, axis tilts and the like, but in a dominant species such as *Homo sapiens* it can generate a new mental ability to cope rationally with concepts hitherto relegated to the region of superstition or abstract thinking. Eventually the frequency of the controlling ego-energy or consciousness becomes so intense that it can no longer tolerate the density of the molecular structure of matter *per se*, and so fails to effect the close atomic binding necessary to the physical experience. By this time, however, the planet or cosmic 'location' in question would be nearing the end of its physical evolutionary cycle, and from there onwards we can hand it over to the physicists to explain how a system eventually 'dies' as the energy of its star is depleted.

Working on the premise that all matter is frozen energy, when translated into terms of waves, the heavier atomic substances could be seen as equating with the longer waves or deeper phases, and the finer frequencies with the shorter and shallower wavebands (see also p. 162). Solid energy occupies space, and in so doing it engages the element of time, or rather utilizes the momentum of time to propel it forward in its evolutionary cycle, in much the same way that we move through time's energy bands on our journey through life. Either way, this very process is energy-inducing in itself.

Space, like time, is also allied to one level of experience – the material or solid world of matter. Space is really an illusion, although matter moves through it, or *appears* to do so as with the receding universe. Are we then suggesting that once divorced from the confines of matter the mind is capable of travelling at the speed of thought to any cosmic frequency? In theory, yes. But in practice it simply does not work that way. There is a whole psychology attached to the reasons why not, some of which we have already touched on, and which are concerned with such issues as religious and social conditioning, individuation, and cosmic maturity. There is also believed to be a kind of ring-pass-not, touched on in the preceding chapter, that is decided by the governing emphases behind the evolutionary programme of any species. But since it is time, as it relates to ourselves in the context of the world we know as 'real' that we are concerned with for the moment, such complex issues must needs be abandoned temporarily.

So much for the metaphysics. Our next step is to relate the aforementioned to events as we are able to observe them in the 'now'. If we subscribe to the belief that our life on Earth has some purpose, then it is worth considering that time acts as a springboard for both the physical and spiritual evolutionary progress of all species. Chaos is represented by the disorder of the evolving consciousness which employs the energies of time as a refining process through which to pass *en route* to its ascent to finer and faster frequencies. The entropic disorder of the human physical system is observable in the ageing process *in one pocket of time only*, that is the observable present. When the particle (body) ceases to be observably manifest, its wave aspect assumes temporary dominance, since it is no longer affected by gravity as Penrose suggests. Once in the chaotic realms of timelessness it becomes accentuated, just as its particle aspect was accentuated while in the world of matter. Time's energy encompasses both of these worlds, and is as equally manifest in timelessness as it is in the physical universe.

In terms of human, and all other states of consciousness, each time period, be it in the physical or non-physical worlds, offers a specific experience that is unique to its own ethos. No experience is ever duplicated or repeated. Scientists have also observed this phenomena – Penrose, for example, in his study of quasi-crystals,[8] and Coveney and Highfield, who comment:

> The birth and expansion of the universe also bear testimony to time's arrow. So do the curious decays of the long-lived kaon; the predilection for light waves to spread into the future, not the past; the tendency of things to mix, cool, and decay; and the asymmetry of diversity in the evolutionary tree. Only in an irreversible world are cause and effect distinct, so that a logical narrative of events can be laid down.
>
> Irreversibility permits a spectrum of exciting new possibilities, for it is also crucial to creation and life. Instead of trying to minimise its role, as many have done, we now know how to exploit it.[9]

In the same context, the Greek philosopher Heraclitus said of time: 'You cannot step into the same river twice, for other waters are ever flowing on.'[10] To which I would add – not in *this* universe, anyway.

Parallel Time

But what of other worlds which, according to some physicists, may well accommodate time's reversibility process. For example, were we to be able to progress backwards in time from old age to babyhood, would we pass the same signposts along time's road that we did on our forward journey? I think not, since the same unrepeatability law would apply. Let us consider how irreversibility, as related to time's forward arrow, might work out in a parallel universe. A train crashes because an error of judgement has been made; as a result, several people lose their lives and others are injured or maimed. In another time dimension, or parallel universe, those same people may travel on an identical train, but a mistake will not be made and no one will be killed or injured. Such minute changes are seen by theoretical metaphysicians as offering us the opportunity to correct or alter the pattern of our former errors or choices.

Although one may seem to experience in one time-zone or parallel existence what appears exactly the same as another in dress, custom and material accoutrements, there will always be subtle differences. Some people are actually able to visit these different time-zones in dream state and balance the experiences of one against the other. How many of us have awakened from a disturbing dream to find with great relief that the problems or dangers one has just been facing have no reality in this world? And yet, in some other dimension the wave of fear or apprehension they produced was strong enough to intrude into the reality we call the present, producing pronounced effects in the autonomic nervous system.

It was some years ago when I first discovered that certain of my dream sequences related to an entirely different life from the one I now live. There were some points in common, but the outcomes were vastly different. Now that I have familiarized myself with some of these parallel landscapes, I am able to find my way around them, remember which road leads where, and relate to the people I 'knew' during the drama, but who seldom bear any resemblance to the people in my waking life. Sometimes there is a cross-intrusion, and a relative, friend, or much loved animal will appear with me in an unfamiliar dream scenario. I also dream in shapes and sensations which are in no way connected with life in this physical world. When regressed under hypnosis I have experienced life as a particle from a helium atom, involved in the solar processes taking place in some distant sun. I have also returned to this state in my sleep, and have often wondered how many other people might have shared this experience with me. But then the subject of dreams is so vast that it would take many a book to describe its myriad complexities. Zohar and Marshall would, no doubt, view all this as confirmation of their theory of the interconnectedness of all life, and they might well be right. After all, I have no way of proving that my helium-atom experiences relate to a former state of existence, unique to my own wave particle, as it could equally be argued that I was accessing the universal collective unconscious.

Dreams undoubtedly take us into Outer Time, and from thence to the multiple existences of parallel lives. The late John William Dunne, who paved the path for many a time-seeker with his masterly work *An Experiment with Time*, concluded that, far from being a mere chronology, time existed in other, more subtle forms. Dunne, an aeronautical engineer, based his ideas on a series of precognitive dreams, and although his perceptions were valid and his research meticulous, when he published his findings in the 1920s they were dismissed out of hand by layman and scientist alike. Since those days, however, the validity of his observations has been confirmed in many areas of research, from quantum physics to parapsychology.

Dunne's premise was that time does not appear to be wholly finite and measurable and that, as an energy, it exists in aspects or at frequencies that do not concur with the standard concept of chronology. Many of Dunne's dream experiences were viewed with suspicion at the time, but having read his book I can vouch for the fact that such 'coincidences' do take place. They have indeed occurred for me, and from my earliest childhood. Before I could even walk I can recall dreaming I was a mature adult with an adult's lucidity and comprehension. In fact, I never dreamed that I was a child at all. Once I went to sleep I was someone else completely, who could move around through time and space and observe the affairs taking place in the world at the time (in the 1930s). These I would often relate to my nanny the following day, and they were inevitably precognitive. One particular dream I had during childhood was not 'fulfilled' until years after the Second World War, when I chanced to see a piece of old film on television. It was like an exact replay of my childhood dream!

Dunne dismissed the idea of clairvoyance, mediumship or telepathy, tending to view his nocturnal experiences as a kind of foreknowledge of his own life and actions. When commenting on these phenomena in her book *The Mask of Time*, Joan Foreman observed that that either Dunne's dreams were anticipating his future, or the future (time?) was transmitting the information to him *backwards*. She concludes:

> If the former supposition is true, then the future must have been already existent for it to have been anticipated; if the latter is correct then an existent future must also be supposed in order that it may transmit its own details back to the present. So in either case a future exists in detail while the subject is still some way, in terms of chronological time, from his own passage through the particular part of it notified to him. The present is known because it is being lived through; the past is known because it has already been lived through; and the future can be known because it is already there.[11]

Ms Foreman's book is rich with interesting anecdotes of precognition, time slips, and the teachings of the various mystics who have emphasized the relevancy of time as far as their philosophy is concerned: Gurdjieff, Ouspensky, Maurice Nicholl, J. G. Bennett, T. S. Eliot, and more recently Lyall Watson and J. B. Priestley. Priestley's concept of time is an interesting one in that it accommodates the possibility of mind controlling time. He conceived of time as a threeway division: Time One, clock time; Time Two, dreams, possibilities and the enfolding future; and Time Three, creative imagination in which will and execution are united, and wherein the power of imagination or visualization can become the reality and not simply an escape from the 'now' time.[12]

For those interested in Dunne and his experiments, in addition to the aforementioned classic, his other works relative to the study include *The Serial Universe, Nothing Dies, Intrusions?*, and *The New Mortality*. In the latter work he notes 'the marked intuitive awareness shown by the human race of the part played by time in its affairs'.[13] Personally, I find some of Dunne's writing somewhat obscure. Once deciphered, however, the truth of his assumptions shines boldly through. Foreman, on the other hand, is a joy to read and I have no hesitation in thoroughly recommending her book.

Time, the Universe, and God

Dunne conceived of time as an entity in its own right, while in more recent times it has also been seen as a fourth, fifth or sixth dimension, a process, a series of levels, and so forth. Unlike the peoples of ancient days, most of us have failed to clothe it with a specific identity, although we comment freely on its presence with such everyday sayings as 'passing time', 'marking time', 'time, the enemy', 'time and tide wait for no man', and many others. For my part, I go along with Dunne. Time *is* a living, conscious, self-regulating entity. Its veins are the circuits along which its energy courses; like the universe, it encompasses the alternations between chaos and order, matter and antimatter, at every conceivable (and as yet many an inconceivable) dimension. It is simultaneously wave and particle, the material universe being but one of its physical manifestations (Inner Time), and the hidden universes its wave aspects or subtle bodies (Outer Time). It is a self-energizing intelligence, whose footfall is gravity and whose voice is sonics. Nuclear energy is its internal conversion system, electrodynamics its fluctuating pulses, and the various 'holes' in space its orifices.

Time is that cosmic law whose forward directional impulses we may either flow with, or fight against. If we flow with them we benefit, but if we elect to push against them we create a temporary energy surge that eventually destroys us. Time is multifaceted, its many faces or aspects vary according to the needs of each individual universe or cosmic frequency through which it is manifesting. It is a duality of both chaos and order, and like the highest common factor it is also the greatest common divisor. Its alchemical, chaotic aspect was observed and commented upon by Jung who highlighted the close and mysterious relationship that exists between the Mercurius, the planetary genius of Mercury, and Saturn the Grim Reaper, both having chaotic and time associations. In Gnosticism, Saturn is the highest archon, the lion-headed Ildabaoth ('child of chaos'); but in alchemy the child of chaos is Mercurius. Jung commented:

> Mylius says that if Mercurius were to be purified, then Lucifer would fall from heaven. A contemporary marginal note in a seventeenth-century treatise in my possession explains the term sulphur, the masculine principle of Mercurius, as *diabolus*. If Mercury is not exactly the Evil One himself, he at least contains him – that is, he is morally neutral, good and evil, or as Kunrath says: 'Good with good, evil with evil.' His nature is more exactly defined, however, if one conceives him as a *process* that begins with evil and ends with good.[14]

Thus the symbol of Mercurius, the Caduceus, features two serpents entwining the central, winged rod, one negative (chaotic), and the other positive (orderly). The fact that the mind is capable of balancing these two forces is shown by the surmounting wings, which represent the transpersonal or Higher Self.

As Jung so wisely comments, the Mercurius (Mercury, Thoth, Sîn, Hermes, Cronus, Aion or any of the gods of time) energies are neutral in that they are dualistic. Although the chaos/order

pendulum may be seen to swing with a degree of periodic regularity throughout the universe, the way any 'mind' or 'intelligence' handles those energies at any given time would appear to bear some influence on its development as a unique entity or, as Jung would say, its individuation. The gods of time were inevitable judges or testers, like Thoth/Tehuti in the Egyptian myth, who was the judge in the recurring combat between the Horus gods of Light or Order and Set, the dark god of Chaos. Likewise, it is Saturn in our birth charts that astrologers believe to be concerned with our deeds in other time zones or parallel universes (past lives in common metaphysical parlance), so it was not without good reason that Shakespeare referred to Time as 'that Old Common Arbitrator'.

Most of the gods of time appear in the masculine gender, and I am often asked why this is so. There are, of course, female time deities, the Egyptian goddesses Seshat and Maat, for example, and the Greek Moerae, Clotho, Lachesis and Atropos that we have discussed in Chapter 6. It is interesting to observe, however, that these are usually associated with the *orderly* side of time, rather than its chaotic mode. Perhaps there is something to be learned from this concerning the feminine role in our particular universe?

When it comes to a consideration of time as a power in its own right, the questions we need to ask ourselves are these: does time really test us or do we utilize it, albeit unconsciously? Are we, ourselves, in fact, the judges of those deeds or misdeeds we carry out during our sojourn along the highways and byways of time? The fact that time exercises a judgemental influence on us was obviously observed by the sages of old, but perhaps it is we, ourselves, prompted by time's energies, who assume the role of Thoth, Cronus, Old Father Time, or whoever, when we come to assess our transpersonal development, or lack thereof, as the case may be.

It could be deduced from the aforementioned that I am seeing Time as God or, perhaps, God as Time. Well, it all depends what you mean by 'God'. Hawking refers to the fallacy pointed out by St Augustine 'of imagining God as a being existing in time: time is a property only of the universe that God created. Presumably he knew what he intended when he set it up.'[15] But what proof (of the scientific kind, of course) do we have that there is a God in the religiously accepted sense of the word, or that God is a *He*? None that I know of, unless the mythical masculine Time characters as discussed above are applied, all of which would appear to embody the chaotic rather than the orderly aspects of time. Time, on the other hand, is a very obvious factor, one particular manifestation of which we may all witness with our physical senses. And although it also has its illusory, or more esoteric aspects, even these may be evidenced in the worlds of quantum, dreams, and the paranormal.

Sir James Jeans hinted at the universe being more like a 'Great Thought' than a 'Great Machine', which is valid metaphysical thinking. But by which name should we know this 'Great Thought?' God? Time? Tehuti was good enough for the ancient Egyptians, Sîn for the Sumerians, Cronus for the Greeks, Aion for the Romans. Could God, therefore, be multifaceted, like time? I cannot personally conceive of a supreme deity in the singular sense, but rather of a multi-aspected intelligence that encompasses all time and whose Mind we, at our present stage of spiritual and somatic evolution are incapable of comprehending. Calling *It* 'He' gives offence to a lot of women to start with, since no one knows for sure whether *It* has a gender. Assuming *It* to be the all-powerful being that some of the major religions would have us believe, logic demands that *It* must encompass *both* masculine and feminine principles in equal proportions. Well, as Alfred North Whitehead said: 'A clash of doctrines is not a disaster, it is an opportunity',[16] whereupon I rest my case!

Endnotes

1. J. Gribbin, *Timewarps*, p. 158.
2. S. Hawking, *A Brief History of Time*, pp. 65–6.
3. P. Davies, *The Cosmic Blueprint*, p. 171.
4. P. Coveney, and R. Highfield, *The Arrow of Time*, p. 293.
5. Davies, *op. cit.* p. 155.
6. *Ibid.* p. 155.
7. F. Capra, *The Tao of Physics*, p. 141.
8. Davies, *op. cit.* p. 79.
9. Coveney and Highfield, *op. cit.* p. 293.
10. A. Tomas, *Beyond the Time Barrier*, p. 21.
11. J. Foreman, *The Mask of Time*, pp. 82–3.
12. *Ibid.* p. 89.
13. *Ibid.* p. 19.
14. C. G. Jung, *Alchemical Studies*, p. 228.
15. Hawking, *op. cit.* p. 166.
16. Coveney and Highfield, *op. cit.* p. 260.

10
Space-time Travel and the Future

> Time present and time past
> Are both perhaps present in time future,
> And time future contained in time past.
> T. S. ELIOT, *The Four Quartets*

Dr John Gribbin, writing in *Timewarps*, expressed the opinion that the best immediate prospect for time travel was the human mind. This does not, of course, mean that physical time travel is beyond the realms of possibility, and its prospects certainly call for exploration.

Space Travel

Closely allied to travel through time is space travel, but not simply to the Moon and back via rocket propulsion. Along with our 'sci-fi' writers, certain far-seeing scientists also have some mind-boggling ideas about our future in the dimensions of space and time. In 1987/88, Charles Pellegrino of Hofstra University, New York, together with James Powell, of the Department of Nuclear Energy at Brookhaven National Laboratories, were investigating the possibilities for interstellar flight using antimatter rockets. Other investigators also joined in, including Robert Jastrow, Professor of Astronomy, at Dartford College in New Hampshire, Jill Tarter, astronomer at NASA, Robert Forward, energy scientist at Hughes Corporation, Malibu, California, and John Rather, Vice-president, Kaman Aerospace Corporation, Arlington, Virginia. According to a report by Paul Simons in the *Guardian* (10 July 1987) Alpha Centauri had been chosen for the maiden flight, being one of our nearest stars a mere 4.3 light years away. In Earth time the space travellers would be away for about thirteen years. But for the crew travelling at near the speed of light, the trip

179

would take only six years, which would include a year at their destination! Simons tells us:

> The ship would accelerate gradually for up to six months, then coast through space at near light speed for more than a year and then decelerate for six months (all these figures are time as perceived by the crew). Once in the vicinity of Alpha Centauri, the crew compartment would be detached from its tether and fly off as a separate spacecraft to explore the area.

Another factor that makes the Alpha Centauri area so interesting is that Alpha Centauri A and B are far enough apart from each other that any planets located in the habitable zones are likely to have stable orbits, so there might well be life there as we know it.

Regarding the kind of propulsion used for such a strange journey, Simons explains: 'The engine driving the interstellar spacecraft is truly out of "Star Trek". It combines matter and antimatter to provide astonishing power. The technology for this is already developing at a rapid pace. . .' The United States have achieved a degree of success in harnessing antiprotons in a magnetic trap, an antiproton being positively instead of negatively charged. But when an antiproton meets a normal, or negatively charged proton their entire masses are converted into energy. Simons further comments: 'To put it into perspective, the conversion of matter to energy is about one hundred times that of a hydrogen bomb.'

I suppose this is a phase through which our Earth technology is obliged to pass, but I can conceive of a future time when this kind of ironmongery will no longer be necessary, and space travellers will be able to sail silently from galaxy to galaxy or universe to universe on time's free energy, employing the forces of antigravity to land on those worlds of matter where time manifests in its observable mode. However, early space explorations will, no doubt, alert our scientists to the existence of time's energies, or they may possibly be told about them by friendly aliens somewhere in the starry firmament we call the sky. There is, however, one consideration we should not lose sight of: when we eventually do visit another inhabited planet, it is *we* who will be the aliens!

Assuming we are preset for a future in the uncharted depths of the cosmos, what about the wear and tear on our physical bodies that would appear to be part of the price paid for the possible knowledge to be gained? Astronauts, we are told, often suffer physically from over-exposure to weightlessness, while their experiences in Outer Time and space are just as likely to cause them mental/psychological problems. It has been postulated that time dilation may produce some curious phenomena. For example, interstellar travellers moving close to the speed of light might well appear differently to each other, while there could conceivably be other physical side-effects that have not so far been considered. There is a logical answer to all this, but since we do not have the technology to cope with it at present, it must lie buried in the future until some enterprising and far-seeing scientist chances upon the time capsule in which this knowledge is concealed.

Time Travel?

The idea of a time machine is nothing new. It was immortalized by H. G. Wells in his novel of the same name. More recently Emile Drouet, a French engineer and astronomer who made a life study of time travel, wrote: 'One must admit that in a few centuries or millennia, voyages in Time will become a reality and a practical possibility.'[1] Like many scientists, Drouet regarded time as static: time stays, we move. Therefore, in order to travel back to the past it is necessary to retrace our steps and find the exact spot the Earth occupied at a specific date. Since the Earth travels round the sun at the speed of 107,181 kph (about 67,000 mph) tracing a spiral as it moves into interstellar space, and the whole system in turn moves through space in the direction of the constellation of Hercules, to a point near Vega, at the velocity of 69,198 kph (about 43,000 mph), this might prove difficult. Besides, how does one get back?

Coveney and Highfield see time travel as a fascinating consequence of relativity, both special and relativistic time dilation permitting –

> time travel of one observer relative to another. Nevertheless, the temporal ordering of events is the same for all observers, even if they cannot agree on a universal 'now': no observer in any state of motion, will see light arrive on the Earth before it shines out of stars.'[2]

It seems that a certain famous logician by the name of Kurt Gödel conceived of a cosmological model of a rotating universe in which, according to Einstein's equations of general relativity, journeys into the past were possible. However, Gödel was quick to point out the bizarre possibilities that could arise, coming face to face with a younger version of oneself, for example, not to mention the 'fragment' or reincarnation factor, which scientists generally, and logicians in particular, tend to dismiss out of hand. The verdict? *Reductio ad absurdum*! Our learned friends, it would seem, have elected to heed the words of Oxford astronomer Cedric Lacey, who wrote: 'Time travel is not permitted in any reasonable cosmological model (but I guess that's the definition of reasonable!)'[3] A little hedging of bets, perhaps?

Wormholes are seen by some scientists, notably John Wheeler, as providing possible pathways through time, but cosmologists and physicists tend to disagree among themselves as to whether the negotiation of a wormhole should be weighed against the background of Newtonian or Einsteinian mechanics, or the quantum properties of matter. If the former, the chances would seem to be nil, while the latter at least suggests a *possibility* that if we fell through the right wormhole we might end up somewhere in the past. But why not the future?

Various thinkers have postulated that there must be simpler ways of probing time other than actually travelling back through it and finding oneself an alien among the 'normal' people of the period. This reopens the question of inter-time telepathy I raised in Chapter 3. Since the EPR paradox (p. 55) and similar experiments have suggested that particles are capable of communicating outside of the normal boundaries of space and time, and thought also appears to function along similar lines, what is to stop us, for example, from communicating telepathically with people who lived thousands of years ago? This being the case, one cannot help wondering how many flashes of inspiration actually resulted from such communications, which might register subliminally on the superconscious?

The same might also be said of time travel from the future to the past. Perhaps more than one stray 'chrononaut' (how's that for a new addition to the dictionary?) has dropped in along many a mystic's 'road to Damascus', or taken pity on some simple girl about her prayers, and provided her with a comforting (or otherwise) peep into the future of the world! I find myself wondering whether the French nobles, who were observed enjoying their afternoon at the Trianon by the Misses Moberley and Jourdain actually *saw* their visitors (p. 66), and if so, was it as apparitions or as real people? Assuming the latter, whatever must they have made of their apparel? I know that if I were suddenly confronted with two people in some strange unfamiliar garb (allowing for the variety of clothes that are permissible in today's world of fashion) my curiosity would be greatly aroused. And were I a French aristocrat, unused to confronting 'commoners' head on, I would have at least asked the servants to investigate. So, perhaps these people from the past simply did not see the two academic ladies in the same way that they were able to see them.

Then there was the incident of the man who saw the Scottish steading (pp. 67–8). He particularly noted that although he hailed them, the people seemed not to see him, whereas the animals responded by looking up and affecting appropriate gestures of acknowledgement. Which brings me to a true story that was related to me first hand, although I am bound by confidence not to indulge the real names of the people concerned.

The wife of a certain middle-aged and highly respected GP started to have a series of recurring dreams that caused her some concern. So clear were these nocturnal wanderings, that she was able to describe the location and the house in which the events took place in great detail. Since a considerable element of fear was attached to the whole sequence, her health became adversely affected, which naturally caused her husband a degree of concern, since she was normally a very rational and well-grounded person. Rather than suggesting that she visit a psychiatrist, and not subscribing to the reincarnation theory that had been proposed by both his partners and several friends, he asked her if she could in any way identify the location of the house that featured in her dream. She told him she was sure it was in France, and that she had a pretty good idea where. 'Then we will go there and lay this ghost once and for all', he declared, and off they went.

During the first two days that they drove around the French countryside no familiar landmarks presented themselves that the wife could associate with her dream. But on day three, while passing through a small village in northern France, she suddenly called her husband's attention to a church, and a road to the left that led past a small copse. From then onwards her directions were clear. There would be a crossroad with one arm of the indicator hanging loose, some farm buildings to the left, and a lane that narrowed into a single track just past three cottages. And sure enough everything was exactly as she described. Following her instructions still further, they found themselves facing a long, private driveway which lead to a large, somewhat Gothic-looking (aren't they always!) house. By that time the wife was extremely fearful, but her husband, being the rationalist that he was, insisted that they call there and settle the matter once and for all.

He rang the doorbell and the squeaky portal was opened by a lady of severe mien, whom he judged to be in late middle age. She greeted him somewhat frostily; then, as she turned to his wife, her face turned ashen and she promptly fainted! In response to the doctor's call for assistance, two other of the house's residents put in an immediate appearance, one turning out to be the lady's son and the other a maid. After she had been carried to a convenient sofa they were joined by other members of the family who were quick to offer an explanation. Their house had been haunted for some months by the ghost of a lady who appeared regularly on the upper landing in the middle of the night, apparently in some state of distress, after which she made her way down the long flight of stairs, sobbing quietly to herself. They had all seen 'her', and the haunting had started to get on the older lady's nerves. Not only did the doctor's wife fit perfectly the description of the spectre they had seen, but the repetitive dream she had related to her husband so many times was exactly as the French family described.

Now this may not relate to time travel in the mechanical sense, but it does substantiate the ability of our wave aspects to travel 'abroad' during sleep, while the more metaphysically inclined of my readers are bound to come up with the suggestion that the doctor's wife had probably lived in that house in a former life, during which some distressing episode had taken place. In fact, the couple enquired of their French hosts as to whether their family had always been the owners. It seemed not, the property having come into their possession via the will of a widowed uncle, about whose private life they knew very little other than that his five-year-old son had died as a result of a fall from the top to the bottom of the staircase, and his wife had passed on 'shortly afterwards, from a broken heart', or at least that was how it had been told to them. But that was all a long, long time ago!

Can an event of this kind be explained in terms acceptable to the dialectic materialist? Perhaps Roger Penrose had the answer in his statement:

Quantum physics involves many highly intriguing and mysterious kinds of behaviour. Not the least of these are the (non-local) quantum correlations which can occur over widely separated distances. It seems to me to be a definite possibility that such things could be playing a role in conscious and thought modes. Perhaps it is not too fanciful to suggest that quantum correlations could be playing an operative role over large regions of the brain. Might there be any relation between a 'state of awareness' and a highly coherent quantum state in the brain? Is the 'oneness' or 'globality' that seems to be a feature of consciousness connected with this? It is somewhat tempting to believe so. [4]

Back in the 1950s I wrote for a magazine a couple of short stories that dealt with the subject of time. The first of these, set in England during the reign of Elizabeth I, told the tale of a young shepherd boy who accidentally came upon a time warp and ended up temporarily in a British airfield during the 'blitz'. The second story was called *The Time Camera*. It concerned a New Zealand boffin who had constructed an electronic gadget that could take photographs *out of time*. His problem, however, lay in the fact that in its present stage of development he had no control over what it might or might not come up with. News of this soon spread via the usual 'bush telegraphs' and soon several agencies, political, religious and commercial, were out to destroy both him and his camera. The story was related in the first person by a cynical reporter, and the tale concluded with an ironic twist.

Nearly twenty years later, when Andrew Tomas' book first appeared, the following statement caught my eye:

> Can past events be photographed after they have occurred? At first the question may seem absurd. But an Associated Press report on 17 August 1958 released via the *Miami Herald* described earth-shaking experiments which the United States Air Force was carrying out at that time.
>
> A special infra-red camera photographed an empty parking lot from a reconnaissance plane. The result was a photograph of cars that had been parked on the spot several hours previously, and which were not there at the time the pictures were taken.[5]

Nowadays we would no doubt ascribe this phenomenon to heat images, but this does not mean that time photography is not a future possibility. We have already explored the feasibility of stones, trees, and even geophysical locations, as time recorders which can be tapped into by those sufficiently sensitive to so do. The British scientist Arthur Clarke was of the opinion that all events might well leave some impression upon the universe at a level that our present technology is incapable of probing. That these ideas would appear to be synchronized in the collective unconscious may be shown in the fact that the well-known science fiction writer Isaac Asimov, in his book *The Dead Past*, also featured a man who invented a neutrino recorder which made time viewing possible.

Myth – Fact or Fiction?

As we have already discussed in Chapter 6, it has frequently been postulated that an advanced knowledge of time, space, sonics, gravity, nuclear power and electrodynamics was once possessed by civilizations that existed during prehistoric epochs. These were later destroyed as our civilization might also be if it does not change its direction in the very near future. Although a modicum of what could possibly be seen as evidence has surfaced in support of this theory, the bulk of information has been culled from the mythology and legends of many lands. Mythology is, as we have learned, rich in allegory, and it was not until comparatively recent years that the tales of Troy, to take one example, have been proven as having a factual base. Jung carried out an extensive study of comparative legend and mythology, which led him to the following conclusion:

> What we are to our inward vision, and what man appears to be *sub specie aeternitatis*, can only be expressed by way of myth. Myth is more individual and expresses life more precisely than does science. Science works with concepts of averages which are far too general to do justice to the subjective variety of an individual life.[6]

Jung's sentiments are re-echoed in the words of the Soviet Professor, I. A. Efremov, who insists that 'historians must pay more respect to ancient traditions and folklore' and accuses scientists in the West of 'a certain snobbishness when it comes to the tales of the so-called common people'.[7] However, assuming that the gates to time's terminals will be opened to us before long, there are bound to be ways in which all these questions may be settled in the not-too-distant future.

Prominent among the sciences believed to have existed in time past is that of sonics. The effect of sound on both the psychology and biorhythms of humans and animals alike has been scientifically oberved for many years. There is also a school of belief that subscribes to the idea that we each have a personal 'keynote', the knowledge of which, were it to fall into the wrong hands, could wreak psychological and physical havoc in our lives. Perhaps this is one of the reasons why my scientist friend, whom I referred to in Chapter 6, was reluctant to pursue that particular line of scientific enquiry.

In his fascinating book *Stalking the Wild Pendulum*, the Czech-born biomedical engineer Itzhak Bentov covers the subject of sound waves and vibrations as related to both time and ASC's. Bentov's theories on time, space, and the quantum worlds were first published in 1976 so he can claim to be among the first to conceive of the particle-wave duality in terms of human consciousness. Like Zohar, Bentov talks of 'wave packets' (electrons and other subatomic particles that are neither fully particles nor fully waves, but a combination of both). He sees the principle of particle-wave duality as holding true not only in the limited area of photons, electrons and nuclear particles, but also in the larger aggregates of matter. Bentov also introduces a theory for the unification of the waves of sound, light, electrodynamics and nuclear radiation, each of which he relates not only to human consciousness but also to the innate consciousness that every animist believes exists in all matter. He tells us:

> Let us look for a moment on the effects of thoughts on things or people. A thought is energy that causes the neurons in the brain to fire in a certain pattern. That naturally produces tiny currents along definite paths in the brain cortex that can be picked up with sensitive instruments through electrodes on the surface of the skull. In other words, a thought that starts out as a tiny stir eventually develops into a full-fledged thought producing at least a 70 millivolt potential some-where in the cortex. It fires the first neuron, which in turn causes others to fire in a certain sequence. However, in this universe no energy is lost. If we can pick up the current produced by the thought outside the head, it means that the energy of the thought was broadcast in the form of electromagnetic waves, and at the velocity of light into the environment and, finally into the cosmos.[8]

In this passage, and in similar statements throughout his book, Bentov reinforces the idea that all systems of energy are co-related, and are not limited in their manifestation to what we might broadly refer to as 'all sentient life'. Therefore, the process of individuation, for example, relates as much to a particle as it does to a flower, a crystal, an animal or a hominid, and con-sequently the universal Time-Mind operates equally throughout the whole of creation – from the minutest particle to the infinity of the cosmos. His theories concerning the relationship between sound and other energy fields were certainly borne out in the research carried out by Nikola Tesla, who was obliged to desist by popular request because his experiments with sonics were adversely affecting the supply of electrical power to the whole of the district in New York in which he lived! It is my own feeling that the hidden mysteries of the science of sonics, like that of time, will eventually re-surface, but perhaps not until humanity has learned that such universal energies are not solely for destructive pur-poses. Or am I pipe-dreaming?

Duality would seem to feature in all the systems we have so far examined, including that of time itself as conceived of in terms of an energy. Since we have the particle-wave aspects of the quantum world at the microscopic end of the scale, it naturally follows that the same principle must also be re-echoed at the wider, macro-cosmic level. Hence my sine-wave theory, which can comfortably be applied to all energy sources, including those of time and the universe itself.

If we are to conceive of time as an energy, personalized or otherwise, and those qualified to comment have intimated that few of us are sufficiently conscious to comprehend what is going on around us, let alone use our minds positively to employ time's energies in a constructive manner, does this mean that we are no more than dice in the hands of time? Several years ago I recall seeing a film called *Jason and the Argonauts* in which the gods of Olympus engaged in a game of chess, the pieces of which were the various heroes engaged in a particular quest. First Zeus moved his piece, causing the 'clashing rocks' to close in on Jason's vessel, but Hera countered his move, prompting Poseidon to arise from the sea and hold back the offending cliffs, while the little craft sailed safely beneath his seaweed-bedecked armpit. I recall being deeply moved by the scene and questioning how much autonomy or free will we really do have? Many, many years later I arrived at the conclusion that, for the most part, we are pawns in the game of the gods – and that goes for time too, *as long as we allow this to take place*. However, extracting oneself from such a situation is easier said than done, and demands a complete new set of mind-pro-gramming. Besides, our quantum selves might well be part of some quantum 'group-self', in which case there will be not only ourselves as individuals to consider, but those others who, by virtue of some transcendental linkage, will be travelling the same cosmic path. In other words, we might well not be islands unto ourselves but, like players in a well-trained and finely tuned orchestra, we are contributors to the harmony of the whole performance.

Mind Travel, Prophecy, and the Future

I have hinted in different places in this book that I was born with a pre-knowledge of certain things and events. Over the sixty-two years of linear time that have constituted my life to date, I have often been able to 'remember the future', or as some people might prefer to say, 'recall the past'. Bearing this in mind, I will obviously not be allowed to end this book without rendering a few prognos-tications concerning the destiny of this planet we call Earth. 'In for a penny, in for a pound', as the saying goes, so here we go:

1. The world is *not* going to end, greenhouse effect or no, although I tend to concur with James Lovelock that Gaia might well tire of her errant brood and elect to eject large numbers of us to seek other cosmic nurseries, until such times as we have matured sufficiently to understand a little more about the cosmic whole. I would include in this category *all* those who suffer from the 'closed-mind syndrome', whatever their persuasion or scientific leaning (and that might well include yours truly!). Of course, Mother Gaia and Uncle Time may well disagree with my assessment, so in the final analysis we will have to wait and see which way the scales fall or the pendulum swings, as the case may be.

2. I believe there will be a major, violent and catastrophic alteration in the orbit or axis of Earth which will result in a change in the positions of the poles and equator. When? I haven't a clue! But I have 'seen' it quite clearly, and as I very much doubt whether I shall be displaying my own particle aspect in the observation mode at the time, I shall enjoy the silence of my black hole, or rejoice in my return to my native universe many light years hence. Mind you, I shall send lots of kind and caring thoughts to dear Gaia, and trust that time will heal the wounds that humans have continued to inflict upon her and their own kind, as well as on the other life forms to which she gives succour.

   However I am by no means alone in this presentiment, and I am not referring to the numerous prophecies that regularly appear from psi sources. During the 1960s I was privileged to be invited to tea by the eminent German-born psychiatrist, Dr Charlotte Wolfe. During the course of our conversation the subject of dreams inevitably reared its head, and I mentioned to her a recurring dream that I had had of a major axis tilt. She assured me I was by no means alone in this, and that the same dream was being experienced by people all over the world. In fact, she declared that several men and women of distinction and influence had sought her professional advice in the matter, believing themselves to be suffering from a form of 'night delusion'. She had told them, as she told me, that future events in world history inevitably cast their shadows, and since they are already known in the collective unconscious it is highly likely that any person of sensitivity and social awareness could access such information during sleep state or ASC's.

3. A Grand Unified Theory (GUT) will eventually be acknowledged, along the lines proposed by Lederman and Schramm,

but with a few surprises in store. Mankind will step out into interstellar space, and in so doing, he will finally come to understand the value of the power of thought and how to use it. Will all this make him perfect? Far from it! At each and every level of evolution there will be problems and pitfalls, only they will be somewhat different from those he is encountering today.

4. And these are my final words. There will be a time in the future of Earth when its inhabitants will harness time's energies and thus open up a whole new field of scientific and metaphysical experience. The sleepers will be awakened from their state of unconscious subservience to collective or group thinking. Since the annals of the past will be opened to them, they will be able to reassess their religious, cultural and sociological beliefs and preferences in the light of what *really* took place and not what successive generations of power seekers have hammered into them. A fuller realization of the oneness of all life, and the consciousness that exists in even the tiniest cell, will help all Gaia's children to coexist in harmony and understanding.

Should you, dear reader, fall into the category of those who view as utterly boring a world in which the virtues of peace, love, caring, understanding and harmony predominate then you have my sympathy, as your fragments are likely to be attracted to a succession of trying existences among some war-like, hedonistic race in the region of Orion, or wherever. But because chaos is eventually self-organizing, Gaia may well be only too happy to welcome her prodigal brood back home after the indignities they have inflicted upon her person are long forgotten for, as the saying goes, 'Time heals all!'

Endnotes

1. A. Tomas, *Beyond the Time Barrier*, p. 48.
2. P. Coveney, and R. Highfield, *The Arrow of Time*, p. 103.
3. *Ibid.* p. 104.
4. D. Zohar, *The Quantum Self*, p. 61.
5. Tomas, *op. cit.* p. 51.
6. C. G. Jung, *Memories, Dreams and Reflections*, p. 17.
7. A. Tomas, *Atlantis, From Legend to Discovery*, p. 27.
8. I. Bentov, *Stalking the Wild Pendulum*, p. 100.

Glossary

Akasha. From the Sanskrit *Akasa*, which means 'soniferous ether' (metaphysics), one of the five elementary principles of nature. The word was borrowed by Pythagoras who applied it to the fifth element of quintessence (the basic four being air, fire, earth and water). He taught that a celestial ether of astral light fills all space. His followers decreed that every action and thought that takes place in the physical world is recorded in the celestial medium (the Akashic Records) and the idea has been observed in metaphysical studies ever since. Pythagoras is believed to have gleaned his information from the Orpheun schools, which carried a decidedly Oriental flavour, although the concept is believed to predate these by many centuries.

Antimatter (Antiparticle). In the world of matter, each particle has a corresponding antiparticle. When one particle collides with its antiparticle, both are annihilated, leaving only a discharge of energy in the form of a gamma ray.

Aquarian Age. In astrology, an age is a period of approximately 2160 years, or one-twelfth of the solar cycle of about 25,900 years, which is roughly the time required for the point of vernal equinox in precession to travel all around the zodiac. As the twentieth century draws to a close this point, which is always zero degrees of Aries, is on the verge of leaving the Piscean Age. Precession moves backwards along the zodiacal belt, so when the point of vernal equinox reaches the constellation of Aquarius, we will enter the Aquarian Age proper. Since the constellations have no precise boundaries, there is disagreement among astrologers as to the exact point at which we enter Aquarius. The beginnings and endings of each age are, therefore, only approximate.

Copenhagen Interpretation. Initiated by the Danish scientist Nils Bohr, seen as the progenitor of quantum physics. According to the Bohr school, objects no longer have the same attributes ascribed to them by Newtonian physics.

Cosmology. The theory of the birth, growth and development of the universe.

Determinism. The doctrine that events are completely determined by previous causes rather than being affected by free will or random factors. Determinism falls in with Newton's theory of gravity, and was much favoured by the French scientist the Marquis de Laplace at the commencement of the nineteenth century. The scientific doctrine of determinism gave offence to many people who saw it as infringing both individual free will and the possibility of divine intervention in worldly affairs.

Electromagnetic Field. The field of force associated with an accelerating electric charge, having both electric and magnetic components and containing a definite amount of electromagnetic energy.

Electromagnetic Spectrum. The entire range of radiation extending in frequency approximately from 10^{21} hertz to 0 hertz (or in corresponding wave lengths from 10^{-13} metre to infinity) and including, in order of decreasing

191

frequency, gamma rays, X-rays, ultraviolet radiation, visible light, infrared radiation, microwaves and radiowaves.

The Enemy. A personalized aspect of time which, at the everyday level, usually indicates the limitations imposed by the passage of time: one has insufficient time to fulfil a designated task, be punctual for an appointment, and so forth. In the scientific context, however, it makes more sense, since the passage of time inevitably involves the action of entropy which, in the human system, manifests as the ageing process.

Entropy From the Greek, *en* (in) and *trope* (turning). The transition from order to disorder or dissolution following organization.

1. A measure of the capacity of a system to undergo spontaneous change, thermodynamically specified by the relationship $dS=dQ/T$, where dS is an infinitesimal change in the measure for a system absorbing an infinitesimal quantity of heat dQ at thermodynamic temperature T.
2. The tendency of the energy of a closed system, including that of the universe itself, to become less available to do work with the passage of time.
3. A measure of the randomness, disorder, or chaos in a system specified in statistical mechanics by the relationship $S=k\ln P+c$ where S is the value of the measure for a system in a given state. P is the probability of the occurrence of that state, k is the Boltzmann constant, and c is an arbitrary constant. (*The Reader's Digest Great Illustrated Dictionary*)

Epagomenal. From the Greek *epagomenos* (*epi* – upon, *agein* – to bring). The intercalculated or intercalary days that formed no part of the month of the old solar year. The Egyptian gods worshipped on those days.

Experimenter Effect. Parapsychologists working on research programmes that are designed to prove (or disprove) the existence of paranormal phenomena have observed that whoever is conducting the experiment is in some way able to affect its outcome. Observers noticed that when a test was set up by an ardent disbeliever, the results achieved were abnormally low, whereas the accuracy of the performances of the subjects increased dramatically under the direction of a scientist or researcher who wanted to believe.

Fermion. A particle, such as an electron, proton or neutron, which obeys the rule that the wave function of several identical particles changes sign when the coordinates of any pair are interchanged; it therefore obeys the Pauli Exclusion Principle.

Fractals. In computer science, the family of shapes and irregular patterns – jagged, tangled, twisted, splintered and fractured – that are believed to represent the organizing principle in nature also referred to as 'the geometry of nature'. A specified way of calculating the fractional dimension of real objects, pioneered by Benoit Mandelbrot. Needing a name to describe his shapes, dimensions and geometry, Mandelbrot thumbed through his son's Latin dictionary and came across the adjective *fractus*, from the verb *frangere*, to break. The resonance of the main English cognates -*fracture* and *fraction* seemed appropriate. Mandelbrot created the word (noun and adjective, English and French) *fractal*. (Gleick p. 98.)

'Fractals display the characteristic feature of self-similiarity – an unending series of motifs within motifs repeated at all length scales.' (Coveney and Highfield. p. 362)

Fractals are seen by some scientists to be a way of viewing infinity, or a way of giving some recognizable form to the abstract.

Gaia Hypothesis. Professor Sir James Lovelock's concept of the Earth as a self-regulating entity in its own right, which Lovelock has chosen to refer to by the old Greek mythological name of Gaia. (Ref: *Gaia – A New Look at Life on Earth* and *The Ages of Gaia*, Oxford University Press). The Gaian theory has a large following, many of whom subscribe to the idea that Gaia is also a living intelligence that is fully cognitive of what is taking place on her surface.

Hologram. The pattern produced on a photosensitive medium that has been exposed to holography and then photographically developed. The resulting image appears to exist in three full dimensions and can therefore be viewed from many angles; with each change in viewing angle the image changes accordingly.

Holography. The process that employs film and laser light to record and project three-dimensional images.

Inner Time. Linear time, the time we see on our clocks that is decided by the movement of our planet in relation to the sun.

Karma. From Hinduism and Buddhism, usually defined as the principle of retributive justice determining a person's state of life, and the state of his or her reincarnations as the effect of past deeds. The concept of karma, which is based on the 'As ye sow so shall ye reap' principle, can also be read as a popular metaphysical variation of the 'sins of the fathers' theme, the idea being that we will be required to return to atone for those misdeeds we have perpetrated in previous lives (assuming an acceptance of the linear reincarnation theory, which your author does not). See also Fragment Theory in Chapter 8.

Light (speed of). Usually given as about 186,000 miles (about 300,000 kilometres) per second. In free space the velocity is 2.997925×10^8 ms^{-1}.

Multidimensional Awareness. The ability to compute mentally more than one state of reality, or time zone, simultaneously.

Newton's Laws of Motion. Three laws describing motion, used as the basis for Newtonian mechanics. They are: a body continues in a state of rest of uniform motion in a straight line unless it is acted on by external forces; the rate of change of momentum of a body is proportional to the external force; any force (*action*) on a system gives rise to an equal and opposite force (*reaction*).

Non-locality. The principle that something can be affected in the absence of a local cause. In quantum physics, non-locality is seen as clearly manifest in the EPR paradox experiment, in which two particles interact and then separate at a great distance. Measurements performed on one particle were observed to affect the other in spite of their distance apart. In other words, both particles were not sharing the same locality. For fuller details, see Chapter 3.

Outer Time. (Metaphysics). The non-linear time that exists beyond the confines of our own little corner of the universe, also the timelessness, a state which is believed to exist in the subtle dimensions, and experienced when the psyche is freed from the Inner Time cycle of the physical world or worlds. See also page 2.

Pauli Exclusion Principle. The principle that no two fermions of the same kind may simultaneously occupy the same quantum state.

Periodicity. The quality of being periodic. Recurrence at regular intervals.

Planck's Law. The law that forms the basis of quantum theory. The energy of electromagnetic radiation is confined to small indivisible packets of 'photons', each of which has an energy $h\nu$, where ν is the frequency of the radiation and h is the Planck constant.

Psi. A blanket term used in parapsychology which covers the fields of telepathy, extrasensory perception, clairvoyance, precognition and psychokinesis (PK – mind over matter), and associated phenomena.

Quantum Leap. Any abrupt change or step from one level or category to a quite different one, especially in knowledge or information. Also called quantum jump. See also page 66.

Quantum Theory. Devised by the German physicist Max (Karl Ernst Ludwig) Planck (1858–1947) while professor at the University of Berlin (1889–1928). Planck's quantum theory, which won him the Nobel prize (1918) was applied by Einstein, Bohr and others to transform twentieth-century physics. The theory involved a departure from Newtonian classical mechanics involving the principle that certain physical quantities can only assume discrete values.

Quarternion (Maths) The division algebra over the real number generated by elements.

Quarternion algebra. Any four-dimensional non-associative algebra over a field F, obtained by the Cayley-Dickinson process from a two-dimensional non-association algebra, over F consisting of either the direct sum of F with itself or a separate quadratic field over F: this generalizes the concept of quarternions.

Redshift. The amount by which the wave lengths of light and other forms of electromagnetic radiation from distant galaxies are increased.

Simultaneity. To be truly simultaneous events must occur not only at the same time but also at the same place. For example, an event on Jupiter might be observed to occur simultaneously with an event on Earth. However, as the two events occur in different frames of reference, and as the information cannot travel from one frame of reference to the other faster than the speed of light, the two events would not, in fact, have occurred simultaneously.

Singularity. 'A point in space-time at which the space-time curvature becomes infinite, theoretically the ultimate fate of matter within the event horizon of a black hole. A naked singularity is a singularity not surrounded by a black hole' (Hawking). 'Singularities are predicted to arise inside of black holes at their very centres.' (Wolf). 'Singularities are entry and exit points of that which is beyond space-time projecting into space-time itself.' (Gribbin).

Sonic. 1. Of or relating to audible sound: a sonic wave, 2. Having a speed approaching or being that of sound in air, approximately 332 metres per second (738 mph) at sea level. From the Latin, *son(us)* – sound.

Sonics. The study of the application of sound waves as a form of energy.

Teleology. 1. The philosophical study of manifestations of design or purpose in natural processes or occurrences. (Compare *dysteleology*.) 2. Such overall purpose or design as exhibited in natural phenomena. 3. The doctrine that such overall purpose or design underlies and determines natural processes.

Thermodynamics. *The First Law of Thermodynamics*: heat is a form of energy and in a closed system the total amount of energy of all kinds is constant.

The Second Law of Thermodynamics: this deals with the direction in which any chemical or physical process takes place, and involves Carnot's cycle and the *entropy* referred to by Professor Davies. A simple explanation of entropy would be a thermodynamic quantity that changes in a reversible process by an amount equal to the heat absorbed or emitted, divided by the thermodynamic temperature. However, there are several permutations, the *Boltzmann entropy hypothesis* being one of the better known.

The Third Law of Thermodynamics which is also concerned with a process called 'enthalpy' – total heat – is a thermodynamic function of a system equal to the sum of its internal energy.

Time and Motion.   *Newton's mechanics:* The branch of physics dealing with motion (dynamics).
Einstein's special and general theories of relativity: which describe motion and gravity.
Quantum mechanics: The laws governing the worlds of atoms and molecules.
Thermodynamics: Deals with heat change and energy conservation.
Chaos: Where apparently random behaviour is ruled by deterministic laws.
Evolution: Explains the development of the various life forms on Earth over successive generations.

Time dilation.   A consequence of special relativity. According to this phenomenon, if two observers are moving at constant velocity relative to each other, it will appear to each that the other's clocks have been slowed down. This affects the concept of simultaneity.

Uncertainty Principle.   Also called the principle of indeterminism, which reflects the inability to predict the future based on the past or present. First proposed by Werner Heisenberg (1901–76) around 1926 or 1927, it has become the cornerstone of quantum physics and provides an understanding of why the world is made up of events that cannot be related entirely to the laws of cause and effect. In quantum terms, it claims that one can 'never be exactly sure of both the position and velocity of a particle, the more accurately one knows one, the less accurately one can know the other.' (Hawking, p. 187). Sir Arthur Eddington's amusing comment on the uncertainty principle was: 'Something unknown is doing we don't know what.' See also page 16.

Bibliography

Bentov, Itzhak. *Stalking The Wild Pendulum*, Fontana/Collins, London 1977.

Bergson, H. L. *Time and Freewill,* Macmillan, London 1911.

Berlitz, Charles. *Atlantis*, Macmillan, London 1984.

Bohm, David. *Wholeness and the Implicate Order*, Routledge and Kegan Paul, London 1983.

Capra, Fritjof. *The Tao of Physics,* Fontana Paperbacks, London 1985.

Coveney, P. and Highfield, R. *The Arrow of Time*, W. H. Allen, London 1990.

Davies, Paul. *The Cosmic Blueprint*, Unwin Paperbacks, London 1989.

Davies, Paul. *Other Worlds*, J. M. Dent and Sons Ltd, London 1981.

Dunne, J. W. *An Experiment With Time*, Faber and Faber, London 1958.

Eysenck, Hans J. and Sargent, Carl. *Explaining the Unexplained*, Weidenfeld and Nicolson, London 1982.

Fiore, Edith. *You Have Been Here Before*, Sphere Books, London 1980.

Foreman, Joan. *The Mask of Time*, Corgi Books, London 1989.

Gauquelin, M. *The Cosmic Clocks*, Granada Publications, St Albans 1980.

Gleick, James. *Chaos*, Heinemann, London 1987.

Gribbin, John. *Timewarps*, Sphere Books, London 1979.

Hawking, Stephen. *A Brief History of Time*, Bantam Press, London 1988.

Hope, Murry. *Atlantis – Myth or Reality?* Penguin/Arkana, London 1991.

Hope, Murry. *Ancient Egypt: The Sirius Connection*, Element Books, Shaftesbury 1990.

Hope, Murry. *The Lion People,* Thoth Publications, Loughborough 1985.

Hoyle, F. *The Intelligent Universe,* Michael Joseph, London 1983.

Ivimy, John. *The Sphinx and the Megaliths*, Abacus Books, London 1976.

Jung, C. G. *Alchemical Studies*, Routledge and Kegan Paul, London 1983.

Jung, C. G. *The Archetypes and the Collective Unconscious*, Routledge and Kegan Paul, London 1979.

Jung, C. G. *Memories, Dreams and Reflections*, Routledge and Kegan Paul, London 1973.

196

Jung, C. G. *Synchronicity*, (Picador Edition), Routledge and Kegan Paul, London 1972.

Jung, C. G. *The Structure and Dynamics of the Psyche*, Routledge and Kegan Paul, London 1960.

Lederman, L. M. and Schramm, D. M., *From Quarks to the Cosmos*, Scientific American Library, New York 1989.

Lemesurier, Peter. *The Great Pyramid Decoded*, Compton Russell Element, Tisbury 1977.

Man, John, (ed.) *The Encyclopedia of Space Travel and Astronomy*, Octopus Books, London 1979.

Mead, G. R. S. *Fragments of a Faith Forgotten*, John M. Watkins, London 1931.

Mead, G. R. S. *Thrice Greatest Hermes* Vols 1, 2 and 3, The Theosophical Publishing Society, London 1906.

Moberley, A. and Jourdain, E. *An Adventure*, Faber and Faber, London 1937.

Mooney, Richard. *Gods of Air and Darkness*, Souvenir Press, London 1975.

Mooney, Richard. *Colony Earth*, Souvenir Press, London 1974.

Musaios. *The Lion Path*, 4th Edition, Golden Sceptre Publishing, 1442-A Walnut St., Berkeley, CA 1990.

Musès, Charles. *Destiny and Control in Human Systems*, Kluwer-Nijhoff Publishing, Dorchester 1985.

Pitt, Valerie E. (ed.) *A Dictionary of Physics*, Penguin, London 1988.

Radford, Edwin. *Encyclopedia of Superstitions*, (edited and revised by Christina Hole), Hutchinson, London 1961.

Sagan, Carl. *Cosmos*, Random House, New York, NY 1980.

Schwaller de Lubicz, R. A. *Sacred Science*, Inner Traditions International, Rochester, VT 1961.

Sheldrake, Rupert. *The Presence of the Past* Muller, Blond and White, London 1986.

Sheldrake, Rupert. *A New Science of Life*, Paladin Books, London 1981.

Temple, Robert. *The Sirius Mystery*, Sidgwick and Jackson, London 1976.

Tomas, Andrew. *Beyond the Time Barrier*, Sphere Books, London 1974.

Tomas, Andrew. *We Are Not The First*, Souvenir Press, London 1971.

Wambach, Helen. *Life Before Life*, Bantam Books, New York, NY 1979.

Watson, Lyall. *The Nature of Things*, Hodder and Stoughton, London 1990.

Watson, Lyall. *Dreams of Dragons*, Sceptre Books, London 1986.

Wilber, Ken, (ed.) *Quantum Questions*, Shambhala Publications, Boston, MA 1984.

Wolf, Fred Alan. *Parallel Universes*, Bodley Head Ltd, London 1988.

Zohar, Danah. *The Quantum Self,* Bloomsbury Publishing Ltd, London 1990.

Zohar, Danah. *Through the Time Barrier*, Paladin Books, London 1983.

Index